# BASIC STATISTICAL CONCEPTS

*a self-instructional text*

Jack I. Bradley
James N. McClelland
Long Beach State College

Scott, Foresman and Company

Chicago    Atlanta    Dallas    Palo Alto    Fair Lawn, N.J.

# PREFACE

The basic statistical concepts encountered in the literature of psychology, sociology, and education are presented in this book at a level appropriate for the student taking a first course in one of these subjects. By carefully following the material, students with only minimal preparation in mathematics will be able to comprehend the statistical methods by means of which experimental evidence is weighed, and to understand reports of experiments as they are presented in introductory texts. The book, in providing a background for a critical and objective understanding of research, should lead the student to a fuller appreciation of the subject matter of courses in the behavioral sciences.

The first chapter reviews the arithmetic and algebraic concepts necessary for understanding the topics that follow. Subsequent chapters treat descriptive methods, measures of central tendency and variability, correlation, probability, sampling, reliability, validity, individual differences, and norms. The final section, a criterion test covering all the material, may be used to verify the student's learning and guide him in reviewing portions of the book. The presentation includes some simple mathematical examples and requires a few calculations, but is intended primarily to help the student understand the principles of statistics rather than their mechanics. The time required to read the text and answer the questions varies, but most students are able to complete it in about eight hours.

This programed material has been carefully tested. Students who used only the program were compared with students who read similar material in a standard introductory text and, in addition, received lectures on all or part of the material in their regular classes. Both groups were tested on material common to the program and the text. In every case, students who used only the programed material performed as well as, or better than, students in the other group. It is of course recognized that, because of the novel form of presentation, further experimentation in the use of this type of book is needed. The authors will appreciate suggestions for improvement of either content or method.

The authors wish to express their gratitude to Mrs. Alice Bradley for her editorial comments, to their colleagues at Long Beach State College for help during the testing phase, and to Mr. William Sommerfield, Western Field Editor for Scott, Foresman. Special thanks are due Dr. Chester D. Hull for his work during the development of the mode of presentation.

J. I. B.
J. N. McC.

# CONTENTS

Chapter 1    **Review of Arithmetic and Algebra**                      2

Chapter 2    **Frequency Distributions and Graphs**                   22

Chapter 3    **Measures of Central Tendency**                         34

Chapter 4    **Measures of Variability**                              46

Chapter 5    **The Normal Distribution Curve**                        60

Chapter 6    **Correlation**                                          72

Chapter 7    **Introduction to Probability**                          88

Chapter 8    **Experimental Applications**                           104

Chapter 9    **Reliability and Validity
of Psychological Measures**                                          126

Chapter 10   **Individual Differences and Norms**                    144

             **Criterion Test**                                       160

# INSTRUCTIONS

In this book each pair of facing pages is a unit. The text is on the left-hand pages; the right-hand pages contain questions about the text. Answers to the questions appear in the left column of the right-hand pages. The book is designed to be used as follows:

1. Cover the answer column with a card or a piece of paper, folded so that it does not cover the questions.

2. Read all the material on the left-hand page.

3. Answer the first question on the right-hand page. Write down your answer. Spaces for answers are provided below the questions, but if you plan to go over the questions again for review, you may prefer to write your answers on a separate piece of paper.

4. Slide the card down until the correct answer is revealed.

5. If your answer is correct, proceed to the next question.

6. If your answer is wrong, note the index number beside the correct answer.

7. Find the corresponding index number in the margin of the left-hand page. This number identifies, approximately, the part of the text from which you should have learned the correct response.

8. Reread the appropriate text material until you find the correct answer. Be sure you *understand* the answer before proceeding to the next question.

9. Erase or draw a line through your incorrect answer and write down the correct one. Then go on to the next item.

10. After you are satisfied that you understand all of the material in the unit, go on to the next pair of pages.

# Chapter 1

# REVIEW OF ARITHMETIC
# AND ALGEBRA

1
2

The procedures used in working with numbers are called *operations*.
The fundamental operations in arithmetic are addition, subtraction,
multiplication, and division. All the statistics problems in this
book can be solved by means of these operations.

Each operation has its particular symbol or symbols. The symbol
indicates which operation is to be performed. The symbols most
often used to specify operations are described below.

a. Addition is always indicated by a plus sign (+).

b. Subtraction is always indicated by a minus sign (−).

3

c. Multiplication is indicated in several ways:
1) by a times sign (×), as in 5 × 7,
2) by parentheses, as in 5(7),
3) by a dot, as in 5·7.

4

d. Division is indicated by:
1) a division sign (÷), as in 10 ÷ 2,
2) a horizontal bar, as in

$$\frac{10}{2},$$

3) a slant line, as in 10/2.

5

The sign for equality (=) is placed between two expressions to
indicate that they have the same value. Thus

$$10 + 5 + 2 = 7 + 6 + 4.$$

The procedures used to solve arithmetic problems are known as_____.

1    operations

_____

The four fundamental operations of arithmetic are addition, subtraction, multiplication, and_____.

2    division

_____

The symbols ×, ( ), and · all indicate the operation of_____.

3    multiplication

_____

The symbol ÷, the horizontal bar, and the slant line are all symbols that indicate the operation of_____.

4    division

_____

The sign for equality is_____.

5    =

_____

Numbers may be added or subtracted in any *order* without affecting the result. In examples (a) and (b), the order of the operations is varied but the results remain the same.

1        a. $7 + 5 + 3 + 2 = 17$, and

$3 + 7 + 2 + 5 = 17$.

2        b. $10 - 7 + 2 - 3 = 2$, and

$10 - 3 - 7 + 2 = 2$.

Note that when the order is changed the sign must stay with its number.

3        The order in which numbers are multiplied does not affect the product. In example (c), the order of the operations is changed yet the product remains unchanged.

c. $9 \times 5 \times 3 \times 2 = 270$, and

$2 \times 3 \times 9 \times 5 = 270$.

4        Grouping of numbers in multiplication does not affect the product. The numbers in example (d) have been grouped in different ways without influencing the product.

5        d. $2 \times 3 \times 9 \times 5 = 270$ could also be written

$(2 \times 3)(9 \times 5) = 6 \times 45 = 270$.

6        A number that has a minus or plus sign before it is called a *signed number*. However, a minus or plus sign in front of a number may be taken either as a sign of the number or as a symbol meaning "subtract" or "add." A number with no sign before it is treated as if it had a plus sign before it. Signed numbers are positive if preceded by a plus sign and negative if preceded by a minus sign.

The sums $10 + 3 + 7 + 2$ and $3 + 10 + 2 + 7$ are both _____ .

1    the same (22)

_____

$12 - 10 - 3 + 1$ and $12 + 1 - 3 - 10 =$ _____ .

2    0

_____

The product of a series of numbers does not depend on the _____ in which the numbers are multiplied.

3    order

_____

Grouping of numbers in multiplication does not affect the _____ .

4    product

_____

The product of $7 \times 3 \times 2 \times 6$ and the product of $(2 \times 3)(6 \times 7)$ are _____ .

5    the same (252)

_____

The expression $-5$ can be read either "negative 5" or " _____ 5."

6    subtract (minus)

_____

The expression $7 - 4 - 2$ may be read either, "From seven subtract four and then two to get a result of one," *or*, "To seven add a negative four and a negative two to get a result of one." The result is the same by the two methods.

The rules for combining signed numbers (numbers with a plus or minus in front of them) in the fundamental operations are:

a. To add numbers with like signs, add their values and prefix the common sign.

$$5 + 4 = 9. \qquad\qquad -5 + (-4) = -9.$$

b. To add two numbers with unlike signs, subtract the smaller from the larger and prefix the sign of the larger number.

$$5 + (-4) = 1. \qquad\qquad -5 + 2 = -3.$$

c. To subtract a positive number proceed as in ordinary subtraction.

$$5 - (+3) = 2.$$

d. To subtract a negative number change its sign and add.

$$5 - (-3) = 8.$$

e. The product or quotient of two numbers with the same sign is positive.

$$(+5)(+3) = + 15. \qquad\qquad (-5)(-3) = +15.$$

$$\frac{20}{5} = +4. \qquad\qquad \frac{-20}{-5} = +4.$$

f. The product or quotient of two numbers with different signs is negative.

$$(-5)(+3) = -15. \qquad\qquad (+5)(-3) = -15.$$

$$\frac{-10}{+2} = -5. \qquad\qquad \frac{+10}{-2} = -5.$$

$17 - (+14) =$ _____ .

$17 - (+14) - (+3) =$ _____ .

1   3

_____

     0

_____

$20 - (-10) - (-5) - (+3) = 20 - 10 - 5 - 3.$

2   false

true _____    false _____

The product or quotient of two numbers with the same sign is _____ .

3   positive

_____

$(-7)(-4) =$ _____ .

$\dfrac{-12}{-3} =$ _____ .

4   +28

_____

    +4

_____

The product or quotient of two numbers with unlike signs is _____ .

5   negative

_____

$4(-7) =$ _____ .

$\dfrac{12}{-3} =$ _____ .

6   −28

_____

    −4

_____

1    Simplification of an expression often requires that several kinds of operations be performed. When this is the case, the order in which the operations are performed may be important.

We have seen that numbers may be added or subtracted in any order. Thus when addition and subtraction both occur in an expression, the order in which these operations are performed does not affect the result.

2    In other cases, the order in which kinds of operations are performed may not be optional. For example, the expression $1 + 3/5$ can be read "one and three-fifths," or "one plus three divided by five." If the latter statement is followed, one might make the mistake of adding the one and the three before dividing by five. The original expression, however, indicates that the three must be divided by the five *before* it is added to the one.

To prevent ambiguities of this sort, there are special rules that govern the order in which the operations in an expression are performed. The first of these rules is:

3    a. Division or multiplication *precedes* addition or subtraction unless a different order is specified by the form of the expression.

4        1) $4 + 72 \div 2 = 4 + 36 = 40$. The 72 is divided by the 2 before it is added to the 4.

    2) $15 - 2(6) = 15 - 12 = 3$. The 2 is multiplied by 6, then the product is subtracted from 15.

Simplification of expressions such as

$$\frac{5-2}{6+3}$$

requires application of several _____.

1  operations

_____

When several different fundamental operations are to be employed in simplifying an expression, it makes no difference which operation is performed first.

2  false

true _____    false _____

When operations occur in combinations, the operations of (1) _____ and (2) _____ must be done *after* (3) _____ and (4) _____.

3  addition

1) _____

   subtraction

2) _____

   multiplication

3) _____

   division

4) _____

Simplify $4 + 10 \div 2$.

4  9

_____

Some additional rules governing the order in which fundamental operations are performed are:

1

b. When operations are to be performed in a specific order, the form of the expression must specify the order to be followed. For example,

2

1) Addition and subtraction above and below a division bar precedes the actual division when a fraction is written as follows:

$$\frac{6+9}{2+3} = \frac{15}{5} = 3.$$

3

2) Fractions are simplified before they are added or subtracted.

$$\frac{6}{2} + \frac{9}{3} = 3 + 3 = 6.$$

4

3) If possible, operations within parentheses are accomplished before the parenthetical expressions are further operated upon.

$$5(7 - 3) = 5(4) = 20.$$

5

c. Division may be thought of as the inverse of multiplication. Dividing a number by 4 is the same as multiplying the number by 1/4.

6

$$\frac{8}{4} = 8\left(\frac{1}{4}\right) = \frac{8}{4} = 2.$$

d. When division and multiplication are both specified, either may be done first.

7

$$\frac{6}{3} \times \frac{21}{7} = \frac{6 \times 21}{3 \times 7} = \frac{126}{21} = 6.$$

$$\frac{6}{3} \times \frac{21}{7} = 2 \times 3 = 6.$$

The order in which a group of terms is to be combined, using several operations, must be specified by the _____ of the expression.

1    form

_____

Simplify $\dfrac{3 + 6}{21 - 3}$.

2    $\dfrac{1}{2}$

_____

$\dfrac{12}{24} - \dfrac{9}{3} = \dfrac{3}{21} = \dfrac{1}{7}$.

3    false

true _____    false _____

$4(7 + 6) = 4(13)$.

4    true

true _____    false _____

Division may be thought of as the inverse of _____.

5    multiplication

_____

Multiplying a number by one-eighth is the same as dividing it by _____.

6    8

_____

Simplify $\dfrac{7}{8} \cdot \dfrac{1}{14}$

7    $\dfrac{1}{16}$

_____

The rules for simplifying expressions must be kept in mind when several operations are specified in a single problem. For example, consider the expression

$$\frac{7-2}{7+18} \cdot \frac{8-3}{6\left(\frac{1}{2}\right)}.$$

1    First perform the indicated operations on the numbers in the numerator and denominator of both fractions to obtain the expression

$$\frac{5}{25} \cdot \frac{5}{3}.$$

Then simplify by multiplication and division, in whichever order is most convenient:

$$\frac{1}{5} \cdot \frac{5}{3} = \frac{5}{15} = \frac{1}{3}.$$

2    Note that if both numerator and denominator of a fraction are divided by the same number, the value of the fraction remains the same. In the following example, both numerator and denominator are divided by 7.

3    $$\frac{7}{21} = \frac{1}{3}.$$

Or, for another example,

$$\overset{2}{\underset{1}{\cancel{38}}} \cdot \overset{1}{\underset{3}{\cancel{45}}} = \frac{2}{1} \cdot \frac{1}{3} = \frac{2}{3}.$$

In simplifying

$$\frac{8+4}{13-7} \div \frac{15-7}{6-4},$$

the first step would be to perform the operations of_____ and_____ .

1     addition

       subtraction

Making use of the fact that division is the inverse of multiplication,

$$\frac{12}{6} \div \frac{8}{2}$$

may be converted to a product in the form _____ .

5 (on    $\frac{12}{6} \cdot \frac{2}{8}$
p. 10)

The product

$$\frac{12}{6} \cdot \frac{2}{8}$$

can be simplified by dividing the numerator and denominator of the first fraction by 6 and the numerator and denominator of the second fraction by_____ .

2       2

By then multiplying

$$\frac{2}{1} \cdot \frac{1}{4},$$

and performing one more operation, the expression can be simplified to_____ .

3       $\frac{1}{2}$

1    Often it is desirable to consider the effect of various numbers in an expression without knowing what the actual numbers are. When this is the case, letters are used to symbolize the numbers and we are using algebra.

2    In algebra, letters are used as symbols for numbers and mathematical operations are performed by using the letters instead of the numbers they represent. To put it another way, elementary algebra is an extension of arithmetic in which numbers are represented by other symbols, ordinarily letters.

3    All of the rules of arithmetic thus far considered apply to algebra as well. However, notation is sometimes more cumbersome and simplification somewhat more difficult when symbols are used. Some examples of the application of the rules of fundamental operations to algebraic expressions will serve to make clear the similarities between algebra and arithmetic. Consider

4
$$\frac{12b + 4b - 7b}{3} = ?$$

It isn't necessary to know what number the letter $b$ stands for in order to operate on it mathematically. In algebra, when a number and letter are written side by side it means that they are to be multiplied together. Thus $12b$ means "twelve times $b$" or "twelve $b$'s." In English, the problem above could be read, "twelve $b$'s plus four $b$'s minus seven $b$'s, all divided by three." The given expression is therefore simplified as follows:

5
$$\frac{12b + 4b - 7b}{3} = \frac{9b}{3} = 3b \ .$$

6    Similarly, as in arithmetic, the product or quotient of two numbers (quantities) with unlike signs is negative and the product or quotient of numbers with like signs is positive. Thus

$$(6x)(-8) = -48x, \qquad \text{and} \qquad (-6x)(-8) = +48x \ .$$

It is sometimes convenient in mathematics to use expressions in which letters are used as symbols for_____ .

1  numbers

         —————————————

When letters are used in place of numbers in mathematical operations, we are using algebra instead of_____ .

2  arithmetic

         —————————————

Algebra and arithmetic both make use of the same fundamental_____ .

3  operations

         —————————————

Write in algebraic form: "ten $x$'s plus seven $x$'s minus three $x$'s, all to be divided by two."

4  $\dfrac{10x + 7x - 3x}{2}$

         —————————————

Simplify $\dfrac{10x + 7x - 3x}{2}$ .

5  $\dfrac{14x}{2} = 7x$

         —————————————

Does $3a(-7) = -3(7a)$ ?

6  yes

         —————————————

1   An *exponent* is an instruction to multiply a term by *itself* the number of times the exponent specifies. The exponent is written as a *superscript* (above and to the right of the number it refers to). For example:

   a. $(3)^2 = 3 \cdot 3 = 9$.

   b. $(2y)^3 = 2y \cdot 2y \cdot 2y = 8y^3$.

   c. $\left(-\dfrac{1}{4}\right)^3 = \left(-\dfrac{1}{4}\right)\left(-\dfrac{1}{4}\right)\left(-\dfrac{1}{4}\right) = \left(-\dfrac{1}{64}\right)$.

   d. $\left(\dfrac{1}{x}\right)^2 = \dfrac{1}{x} \cdot \dfrac{1}{x} = \dfrac{1}{x^2}$.

2   Application of the instruction given by the exponent is called *squaring* (where the exponent is 2), *cubing* (where the exponent is 3), or, in general, *raising to a power* (for any value of the exponent).

   a. $b^2$ is read "*b* squared," or, "the second power of *b*."

   b. $c^3$ is read "*c* cubed," or, "the third power of *c*."

3   When a letter is written without an exponent, the exponent is assumed to be 1.

$$y = y^1.$$

4   The *radical* sign ($\sqrt{\phantom{x}}$) indicates that one is to find the square root of the number contained under the sign. The number contained under the sign is called the *radicand*. In the expression $\sqrt{9}$, the radicand is 9. The square root of a radicand is the number that, when squared, equals the radicand. Thus

5   $$\sqrt{9} = 3, \text{ because } 3 \cdot 3 = 9.$$

The same is true in algebraic expressions:

6   $$\sqrt{4y^2} = 2y, \text{ because } 2y \cdot 2y = 4y^2.$$

When a number is to be multiplied by itself, this is usually indicated by a superscript called an _____ .

1    exponent

To indicate that a number is to be squared, the exponent used would be _____ .

2    2

In the expression $x^2 + y + 2$, the exponent of $y$ is assumed to be _____ .

3    1

The symbol used to indicate that one is to find the square root of a number is _____ .

4    a radical ($\sqrt{\phantom{x}}$)

5    4                $\sqrt{16} =$ _____ .

6    $3x$             $\sqrt{9x^2} =$ _____ .

1    A mathematical device of great importance is the *subscript*. When many values of a variable are to be considered, it is not practical to represent each with a different letter. Consider the necessity of representing a whole class of measurements such as a series of test scores. It is convenient to represent the whole set of scores

2    by some letter such as $X$. If it is necessary to treat individual scores, each particular score can be identified by a subscript as $X_1$, $X_2$, $X_3$, and so forth.

The utility and convenience of the subscript is particularly demonstrated when it is used in conjunction with the symbol for summa-

3    tion. This symbol, the upper case Greek letter sigma ($\Sigma$), is used as a sign for the process of adding or summing a series of values.

4    The notation $\Sigma X$ means $(X_1 + X_2 + X_3 + \ldots + X_n)$, or "the sum of all values of $X$ from $X_1$ through $X_n$."

By using $X$ as the *general* symbol for a variable and the subscript to identify a *particular* value, such as $X_3$, the third value, all values

5    of $X$ can be included in the term $\Sigma X$. This term, representing the sum $X_1 + X_2 + X_3 + \ldots + X_n$, is much more brief than one representing each value of the variable separately.

Subscripts help us to differentiate specific values of a_____represented by a given letter.

1    variable    _____

When many quantities are to be represented, we can use a single letter such as $X$ to stand for the quantities in general. Each individual value may then be represented by a_____.

2    subscript    _____

The symbol that means "the sum of all the values" is_____.

3    $\Sigma$    _____

$\Sigma A$ means "add all values of $A$ from $A_1$ through_____.

4    $A_n$    _____

A briefer form for expressing

$$Y_1 + Y_2 + Y_3 + \ldots + Y_n$$

is_____.

5    $\Sigma Y$    _____

1      Letters, representing a series of numerical values, and the symbol
       $\Sigma$, indicating the summation process, are frequently found in statis-
2      tical formulas. Formulas in statistics, like the more familiar
       formulas from elementary mathematics, are equations written with
       letters that represent universal applications. $A = ba$ is the familiar
       formula used in finding the area of a rectangle. In this formula:

$$A = \text{ the area of the rectangle}$$
$$b = \text{ the length of the base}$$
$$a = \text{ the length of the altitude.}$$

3      The formula applies in general for all rectangles; it is applied to
       a particular rectangle by substituting the particular numerical values
       of $b$ and $a$.

       A formula from statistics which represents the mean or average of
       a set of measurements or scores is

$$\bar{X} = \frac{\Sigma X}{N},$$

4      where     $\bar{X} = $ the mean or average value of the $X$ variable
       $\Sigma X = X_1 + X_2 + X_3 + \ldots + X_n$
       $N = $ the number of values of the variable $X$.

       The following chapters will be concerned, primarily, with the com-
       putation of this and other statistical formulas and with the interpre-
       tation of the results. The mathematics involved in these formulas
       are merely further applications of the examples in this chapter.

Statistical formulas frequently include the symbol_____ , the symbol for summation.

1      Σ

Universally applicable relationships among variables may be represented in mathematical_____ .

2      formulas

In a particular application, the letters in a formula are replaced by_____values.

3      numerical

$\Sigma X$ means to_____all the values of $X$ in the application.

4      add (sum)

# Chapter 2

# FREQUENCY DISTRIBUTIONS AND GRAPHS

1   The psychologist often needs standard methods of describing his findings in a short and easily understood way. Statistical methods that fill this need are called *descriptive statistics*.

2   As a result of applying experimental or psychometric techniques, the psychologist obtains a collection of raw data which is usually numerically coded according to some dimension that he assigns. Table 1 presents raw data obtained by recording the test scores of 60 students in an introductory psychology class. Table 1 is a table of raw scores.

## Table 1
### Examination Scores Made by Introductory Psychology Students

| | | | | | |
|---|---|---|---|---|---|
| 57 | 47 | 55 | 52 | 54 | 50 |
| 49 | 59 | 48 | 54 | 56 | 52 |
| 52 | 53 | 51 | 60 | 50 | 49 |
| 54 | 55 | 54 | 53 | 53 | 47 |
| 46 | 55 | 52 | 56 | 55 | 52 |
| 52 | 58 | 57 | 55 | 54 | 49 |
| 56 | 55 | 56 | 58 | 50 | 51 |
| 53 | 50 | 50 | 53 | 55 | 46 |
| 54 | 49 | 55 | 54 | 54 | 52 |
| 45 | 53 | 52 | 53 | 55 | 49 |

3
4   Such a collection of data in raw score form may be important, but it is not of much use in such a disorganized array. By applying certain descriptive statistical techniques, one can organize such data in a more meaningful form.

Statistical methods used to describe data in a short and easily understood manner are called_____ _____.

1    descriptive
     statistics

_____

The first accumulation of coded information is usually recorded as_____data.

2    raw

_____

Original raw data, recorded as they are collected, are difficult to use because they lack_____.

3    organization

_____

Descriptive statistics applied to raw data can be expected to make the material more _____.

4    meaningful

_____

Table 2 includes the same data as Table 1, but the test scores
have been rearranged by applying the sequence of operations listed
below. The result we call a *frequency distribution*. This distribution
shows more clearly the characteristics of the pattern of test scores.

### Table 2
#### Frequency Distribution of Scores on a Psychology Examination

| Score | Tally | f | Score | Tally | f |
|-------|-------|---|-------|-------|---|
| 60 | I | 1 | 52 | 卅III | 8 |
| 59 | I | 1 | 51 | II | 2 |
| 58 | II | 2 | 50 | 卅 | 5 |
| 57 | II | 2 | 49 | 卅 | 5 |
| 56 | IIII | 4 | 48 | I | 1 |
| 55 | 卅IIII | 9 | 47 | II | 2 |
| 54 | 卅III | 8 | 46 | II | 2 |
| 53 | 卅II | 7 | 45 | I | 1 |

Table 2 was constructed from the data in Table 1 by taking the
following steps:

a. First the highest and lowest scores were identified; thus the
limiting values of all the raw scores in Table 1 were obtained.
In this instance the highest score was 60, the lowest 45.

b. All the possible intermediate values were arranged in descend-
ing order.

c. Each score in Table 1 was represented by a tally mark opposite
the same score in Table 2.

d. The tally marks for each score were totaled and the sum entered
as the frequency of occurrence of each particular score. This
column is headed by the symbol *f*, which stands for *frequency*.
Frequency, then, is a statistic that tells us how many times
a given score occurs in a collection of data.

In the procedure used on page 24, the test scores were arranged into a _____ distribution.

1    frequency                    _____

The first step in developing a frequency distribution is to find the_____and _____scores.

2    highest                      _____

     lowest                       _____

The highest and lowest scores in a distribution define the limits within which all the remaining_____must fall.

3    scores (data)                _____

The frequency of occurrence was indicated in the table by making a_____mark opposite each observed score.

4    tally                        _____

The totals of the tally marks opposite each score were recorded in the column headed by the symbol_____, which stands for _____.

5    $f$                          _____

     frequency                   _____

Once the data have been recorded in a frequency distribution, the tally marks are no longer necessary. The $f$ column represents the same information in a briefer form. By totaling the $f$ column, we can determine the total number of scores or cases represented in the frequency distribution. The statistical symbol used to indicate the number of cases is $N$.

Table 3 presents the same data as Table 2, except that the tally marks are omitted and the $f$ column is totaled to indicate $N$, the number of students who took the examination.

### Table 3
### Frequency Distribution of Scores on a Psychology Examination

| Score | $f$ | Score | $f$ |
|-------|-----|-------|-----|
| 60 | 1 | 51 | 2 |
| 59 | 1 | 50 | 5 |
| 58 | 2 | 49 | 5 |
| 57 | 2 | 48 | 1 |
| 56 | 4 | 47 | 2 |
| 55 | 9 | 46 | 2 |
| 54 | 8 | 45 | 1 |
| 53 | 7 | | $N = 60$ |
| 52 | 8 | | |

The symbols $f$ and $N$ are important and will appear repeatedly throughout the remaining lessons. Remember that $f$ means frequency and $N$ means number. Another important symbol in statistics is $X$, which, as we have seen, represents any value of the variable under consideration. In the present example, the test scores are values of the variable. Thus, in this application the symbol $X$ could stand for any such test score.

A frequency distribution does not ordinarily include the _____ marks.

1  tally

_____

The totals of the tallies for each value of the variable in question appear in the _____ column.

2  $f$ (frequency)

_____

The symbol $N$ represents the _____ of cases being represented in the frequency distribution.

3  number

_____

$X$, _____, and _____ are important statistical symbols.

4  $f$

_____

   $N$

_____

The variable under consideration in any study is commonly represented by the symbol _____.

5  $X$

_____

In the example on page 26, a value of the variable is a _____ score.

6  test

_____

In addition to a tabular representation, it is frequently advantageous to represent data graphically. Several methods have been adopted by social scientists, but all have some things in common. Traditionally, the values of the variable are represented on the horizontal axis or *abscissa*. The frequency of occurrence is shown on the vertical axis or *ordinate*. Figure 1 represents the data from Table 3 in graphical form.

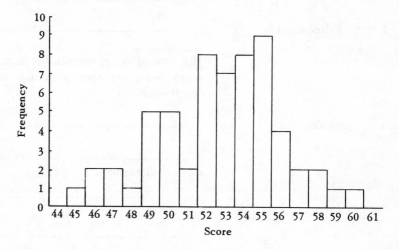

Fig. 1 Distribution of scores on a psychology test.

This graph is called a *histogram* or *bar graph*. It is constructed by drawing a rectangle over each test score. The height of each rectangle indicates the frequency of occurrence of that score. The score values represented on the abscissa or horizontal axis include one additional score below and one above the actual scores obtained by the students in the class.

The abscissa or horizontal axis of a histogram is usually used to represent different values of the_____being measured or observed.

1    variable                            _____

In constructing a histogram it is traditional to use the vertical axis or ordinate to represent the_____ of occurrence.

2    frequency                           _____

A graph that represents the frequency of occurrence of events by a series of adjacent rectangles is called a_____or a _____ _____.

3    histogram                           _____

     bar graph                           _____

Two extra values of the variable are included in a histogram, one_____and one_____than the observed values.

4    higher                              _____

     lower                               _____

1     A graphical presentation of data comparable to the histogram is the *frequency polygon.* It is often used in summarizing data. On first glance it may seem very different from the histogram, but it is quite similar and accomplishes the same purpose. The test scores previously used are presented in a frequency polygon in Figure 2.

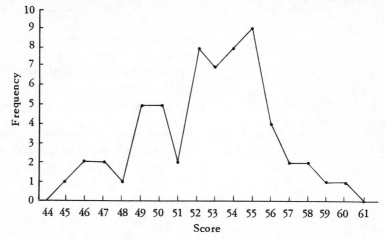

Fig. 2 Distribution of scores on a psychology test.

2     In this application, the frequency is again represented on the ordinate, the test scores on the abscissa. Instead of a rectangular
3     bar, however, a single point representing the frequency of each test score is plotted directly over the appropriate score. Finally,
4     these points are connected in sequence by straight lines. The addition of one higher and one lower score serves to demonstrate that the distribution is complete.

A_____ _____ is a method of graphical representation comparable to the histogram.

1    frequency polygon          _____

The frequency of a score is represented by a rectangular bar in the_____.

2    histogram                  _____

The frequency polygon is a multiple-sided figure whose corners are determined by the _____of each score value.

3    frequency                  _____

The inclusion of two extreme score values with a score frequency of zero indicates that the distribution represented by the frequency polygon is_____.

4    complete                   _____

1      The frequency polygon is particularly useful when two or more distributions are to be presented for comparison on the same graph. An example of this application is shown in Figure 3, in which two sets of test scores are presented simultaneously.

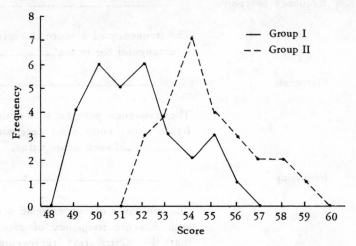

Fig. 3. Frequency polygons of two sets of test scores.

2      When the distributions are superimposed, the two groups can be more easily compared.

When we wish to present more than one distribution of measures on a single graph, it is convenient to use_____ _____.

1        frequency polygons

_____

Superimposing two or more_____on a single graph makes it easier to make a visual comparison of the characteristics of each of the distributions.

2        distributions

_____

# Chapter 3

# MEASURES OF CENTRAL TENDENCY

The behavior of an individual on a particular occasion may, or may not, be typical of him. Therefore it is often necessary to measure his behavior several times in order to get a good estimate of what he is likely to do. For example, suppose a man is being considered for an assignment as an astronaut. It is necessary to make certain he can react quickly to signals from the instruments in his space capsule. To test this, he is asked to press a button when a visual or an auditory signal is presented. His reaction time — the time required to press the button after the presentation of the stimulus — is then measured.

1     Once a measurement of the astronaut's reaction time is obtained, the question is, "Does this reaction time represent his reaction time in general, or is he usually faster or slower?" He may have "jumped the gun" in anticipation of the signal, or he may have been slow in reacting because he was not paying attention. To determine what his typical reaction time is under the experimental conditions, it is necessary to measure several trials and determine the average time required to respond.

2
3     It has been observed that when such a series of reaction times is obtained from a subject, most of the times tend to cluster about some central value, with some slightly longer and some slightly
4     shorter than the more common ones. Statistics that describe the central value about which scores cluster are called *measures of*
5     *central tendency*. A measure of central tendency can be thought of as the average score the individual would get in a large number of trials.

Several _____ of reaction time must be made if the typical reaction time of an individual is to be obtained.

1    measurements

    _____

If several measurements of an individual's reaction time are made, these measures tend to _____ about some central value.

2    cluster

    _____

The description of the experimental measurement of reaction time implies that repeated _____ are not identical.

3    measurements

    _____

A typical value or score about which the scores in a set of measurements cluster is known as a measure of _____ _____.

4    central tendency

    _____

Measures of central tendency are of value because they can be used in predicting the _____ score an individual would get on a _____ number of trials.

5    average

    large

1    To illustrate the problem of obtaining a measure of central tendency, consider an experiment in which a subject moved a control knob whenever he heard a signal. The time between the presentation of the signal and the movement of the knob was measured for twenty trials. The times are given in Table 4.

Table 4
Individual Reaction Times

| Trial | Reaction time (milliseconds) | Trial | Reaction time (milliseconds) |
|---|---|---|---|
| 1 | 213 | 11 | 145 |
| 2 | 206 | 12 | 153 |
| 3 | 132 | 13 | 152 |
| 4 | 185 | 14 | 171 |
| 5 | 160 | 15 | 143 |
| 6 | 153 | 16 | 159 |
| 7 | 153 | 17 | 161 |
| 8 | 155 | 18 | 148 |
| 9 | 150 | 19 | 153 |
| 10 | 139 | 20 | 149 |

2    Although there is quite a range of measurements for this subject, the times seem to cluster around 160 milliseconds. Some times are several milliseconds away from this value, but half are within 10 milliseconds of 160. This clustering of measurements would be more apparent if the raw data were arranged in a frequency distribution.

3    One measure used to describe the central tendency of a group of
4    scores is the arithmetic *mean*. The arithmetic mean is obtained
5    by adding together all of the measurements and dividing by the number of measurements taken. In the example, the sum of the reaction times is 3180 milliseconds. When this total is divided by the number of trials (20), the mean is found to be 159 milliseconds.

The table of reaction times, Table 4, is a collection of _____ data.

1    raw

In order to show the clustering of measurements more clearly, the raw scores should be arranged into a _____ _____ .

2    frequency
     distribution

The first step to take to obtain the arithmetic mean is to _____ all of the measurements obtained.

3    add (sum)

After the obtained measurements have been added together, the mean is found by dividing the sum by the _____ of observations made.

4    number

The measure of central tendency found by dividing the sum of a series of measurements by the number of measurements made is known as the _____ .

5    mean

To express in mathematical terms the method of finding the mean,
a procedure discussed in Chapter 1 is used. Let the letter $X$ stand
for the score on each trial. Thus $X_1$ could stand for the time on the
first trial, $X_2$ the time on the second trial, $X_5$ the time on the fifth
trial, and so on to $X_n$, the $n$th or last score obtained. The arithmetic mean is designated by $\overline{X}$ (read "$X$ bar"), and the formula for
finding the mean is

$$\overline{X} = \frac{X_1 + X_2 + X_3 + \ldots + X_n}{N}.$$

This formula says that, regardless of how many observations are
made, the mean is always equal to the sum of the values for all
of the observations, divided by the number of observations.

The formula presented above is inconveniently long to write, so
it is usually given in a briefer form in which the instruction to add
together all of the $X$'s is indicated by the symbol for summation, $\Sigma$.
The formula then becomes

$$\overline{X} = \frac{\Sigma X}{N}.$$

One must always remember that $\Sigma X$ means "the sum of all the $X$'s."
Substituting values from the reaction-time example, this formula
yields

$$\overline{X} = \frac{\Sigma X}{N} = \frac{3180}{20} = 159 \text{ milliseconds.}$$

In the formula for obtaining the arithmetic mean, the score made by a person on each trial is ordinarily represented by the symbol _____.

1    $X$ (not $x$)

The symbol representing the score made by the subject on his seventh trial would be _____.

2    $X_7$

No matter how many observations are made, the mean is always equal to the _____ of all the scores, divided by the number of scores.

3    sum

$\Sigma X$ means "the _____ _____ all the $X$'s."

5    sum of

The expression

$$\frac{\Sigma X}{N}$$

is often indicated by the symbol _____.

4    $\bar{X}$

1    What has been said about finding the mean reaction time of one subject can also be said about finding the mean reaction time of a group of individuals. In the latter case, the mean for each individual is represented by an $X$ value. Thus the mean time for the first subject $(S_1)$ is represented by $X_1$, the mean for $S_2$ by $X_2$, and the mean for the $n$th subject by $X_n$.

Suppose the mean reaction times of twelve subjects have been obtained by the method used in the earlier example. The means are shown in Table 5.

### Table 5
### Mean Reaction Times for Twelve Subjects

| Subject | Mean reaction time (milliseconds) | Subject | Mean reaction time (milliseconds) |
|---------|-----------------------------------|---------|-----------------------------------|
| A | 160 | G | 152 |
| B | 162 | H | 159 |
| C | 178 | I | 163 |
| D | 154 | J | 160 |
| E | 148 | K | 165 |
| F | 158 | L | 161 |

2
3    Here, the $\overline{X}$ we want is the mean score of the twelve individuals who, in turn, had mean scores as shown in the table. The same formula is used for finding the mean of the group of subjects as for finding the mean scores of each of the individuals:

$$\overline{X} = \frac{\Sigma X}{N} = \frac{1920}{12} = 160 .$$

4    That is, the mean score of a group of individuals is obtained by dividing the sum of their scores by the number of individuals in the group.

The formula for finding the mean score of several subjects is the same as the formula for the mean score of_____ _____ on a series of trials.

1    one subject          _____

The symbol used to represent the mean score of a group of subjects is_____.

2    $\overline{X}$          _____

The number of repetitions of a short poem required for various subjects to learn to perfect recitation were:

| 17 | 11 | 10 | 9 | 6 |
| 14 | 10 | 9 | 8 | 5 |
| 12 | 10 | 9 | 7 | 4 |
| 11 | 10 | 9 | 6 | 3 |

3    20          $N =$_____.

     180          $\Sigma X =$_____.

     9          $\overline{X} =$_____.

The mean score of a group of subjects is the sum of the scores of the subjects times the number of subjects.

4    false          true_____ false_____

1
2
3

A second measure of central tendency is the *median*. The median is the value above which half of the measures lie. It is used when the distribution is badly *skewed* — when the measures are piled up at one end of the distribution rather than being more or less symmetrically distributed about the mean. The difference between symmetrical and skewed distributions can be seen in Figure 4. When a distribution is skewed, the median is a better indicator of the central point about which most of the scores cluster.

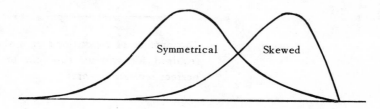

Fig. 4. Symmetrical and skewed distributions.

The achievement test scores from a class of thirty students, some of whom had been promoted without being prepared, appear below.

Table 6
Achievement Test Scores

| 80 | 70 | 67 | 62 | 59 | 38 |
| 77 | 69 | 67 | 62 | 57 | 33 |
| 75 | 69 | 66 | 61 | 53 | 28 |
| 74 | 68 | 65 | 61 | 51 | 19 |
| 70 | 67 | 64 | 60 | 47 | 13 |

4
5

The mean of this distribution is 58, but two-thirds of the students did better than this. The median is 63, since half of the scores are above this value. In this example the median is more indicative of typical performance because the mean unduly emphasizes the performance of the unprepared students.

There is a formula for finding the exact value of the median in cases when it is not as obvious as in the example. However, it is often sufficiently accurate just to rank the measures from high to low (as was done in the example) and count down to the middle of the distribution.

The value below which half of the observed values in a distribution lie is called the _____ .

1    median

The median is not much different from the mean unless the distribution is_____ .

2    skewed

A skewed distribution is one in which the scores are not distributed _____ about the mean.

3    symmetrically

Find the median of the following distribution:

| 27 | 22 | 30 | 20 | 25 |
| 19 | 17 | 20 | 23 | 24 |
| 14 | 14 | 19 | 18 | 23 |
| 20 | 10 | 22 | 24 | 28 |

4    21

When a distribution is badly skewed, the _____ is more indicative of the group's performance than is the_____ .

5    median

     mean

1     A third measure of central tendency is the *mode*. The mode is the score that most frequently occurs. In the distribution of achievement test scores given on page 42, the mode is 67 because more subjects had this score than any other. The mode is seldom used in statistics, but it is a quickly found measure of central tendency, since it can be easily identified without computation. In those cases where typicality is required, the mode provides the necessary information.

2     The concept of modality is useful in describing a distribution that has two very frequent scores, with less frequent scores appearing between them. When this occurs in large distributions it usually means that scores of two unlike groups have been combined in a single distribution. For example, animals of the same species but of different strains often behave very differently on the same task. These differences may be masked if their scores on the task are combined — except that the combined distribution may have two modes, with the scores of one group clustering around one mode and the scores of the other group clustering about another mode.

3     Such distributions are called bimodal; that is, they have two modes.

The following table lists the number of errors made by twenty rats that learned a maze.

### Table 7
### Errors Made in Learning a Maze

| 4 | 8 | 11 | 13 |
|---|---|----|----|
| 6 | 8 | 12 | 14 |
| 7 | 9 | 12 | 15 |
| 8 | 9 | 13 | 16 |
| 8 | 10 | 13 | 18 |

4     The two modes of this distribution are at 8 and 13.

The value most frequently observed in a distribution is called the_____.

1    mode

A distribution with two modes often occurs when scores from unlike_____ have been combined.

2    groups

Distributions having two modes are called _____.

3    bimodal

The modes of the following distribution are at_____ and_____.

| | | | | |
|---|---|---|---|---|
| 1.2 | 1.4 | 1.4 | 1.8 | 1.4 |
| 1.4 | 1.3 | 1.5 | 1.7 | 2.1 |
| 1.7 | 1.8 | 1.3 | 1.9 | 1.1 |
| 1.6 | 1.9 | 1.8 | 2.0 | 1.5 |

4    1.4

     1.8

# Chapter 4

# MEASURES OF VARIABILITY

1 The mean, or some other measure of central tendency, is useful in determining what is representative behavior for an individual or group. It does not provide answers to such questions as, "How much alike were the individuals of the group?" or "How well does the measure of central tendency represent the group?" To answer these questions it is necessary to consider how the values in a distribution *vary* from one another and from the mean. This "spread" or dispersion in a set of measurements is called *variability*.

2 The simplest measure of variability is the *range*. The range is the difference between the two extreme values in the distribution. Consider a distribution of scores (representing trials to an errorless performance) made by a group of girls on a finger maze: 3, 5, 6, 8, 9,

3 9, 11, 12, 13, 14. The range is equal to the highest value minus the lowest value: 14 − 3 = a range of 11.

4 The range is easily calculated, but tells us little about the variability of values *within* the distribution. Compare the distribution of scores made by a group of boys on the same finger maze − 3, 7,

5 8, 8, 9, 9, 9, 9, 10, 11, 11, 14 − with the distribution above. These distributions have the same range and mean, but it is obvious that most of the measurements cluster more closely about the mean in the second distribution than in the first. The amount by which values deviate from the mean is greater in the first distribution.

This example makes it clear that the range does not describe the variability in a group of measurements well enough to clearly distinguish one group from others in which the measures are distributed

6 differently. Thus we need a measure of variability that will take into account every measurement rather than just the highest and lowest.

Measures of central tendency describe the point about which measurements cluster, but other statistics are needed to tell how much the measurements_____ from each other and from the mean.

1    vary

_____

The difference between the highest and lowest measures in a distribution is called the_____.

2    range

_____

The range of the following measurements is_____.

| 202 | 162 | 133 | 104 |
| 184 | 150 | 127 | 99  |
| 176 | 141 | 119 | 97  |

3    105

_____

The range does not describe the deviation of_____values in the distribution.

4    all

_____

The deviation of scores from the mean is greatest in Group_____.

Group A: 5, 10, 15, 20, 25, 30, 35
Group B: 5, 16, 18, 20, 22, 24, 35

5    A

_____

Though two groups of observations have the same mean, the_____of measurements *within* the groups may be different.

6    variability

_____

The variability in a set of measurements depends on how much each score varies from the mean. We can find the difference between a single score and the mean by subtracting the mean from the score.

1

2

The result, the difference between a raw score and the mean, is called a *deviation* score. It is denoted by the symbol x. To indicate that the mean, $\overline{X}$, is to be subtracted from a score, $X$, we write $(X - \overline{X})$. The result is a deviation score, x, so $x = (X - \overline{X})$.

Consider what happens when the girls' scores on the finger maze are converted to deviation scores. First, examine the histogram in Figure 5, which is based on the girls' original scores (3, 5, 6, 8, 9, 9, 11, 12, 13, 14).

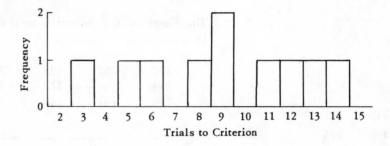

Fig. 5. Performance of girls on a finger maze.

The mean of this distribution is 9. The deviation score equivalent to the lowest raw score, 3, is found by substituting in the formula $x = (X - \overline{X})$. Thus $x = (3 - 9) = -6$. Notice that this deviation score, −6, is also the lowest score in the histogram of deviation scores in Figure 6. In fact, the histogram of deviation scores has exactly the same shape as the histogram of raw scores. Each score is simply represented with a new number that refers to the magnitude of the score's deviation above or below the mean.

3

4

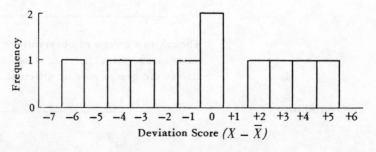

5

Fig. 6. Deviation scores of girls on a finger maze.

A deviation score is found by subtracting the _____ from the raw score.

1    mean                    _____

The symbol for a deviation score or measure is _____ or _____ .

2    $X - \overline{X}$       _____

     $x$                      _____

When a graph of raw scores is compared with a graph of the same data in the form of deviation scores the shape of the graphs is _____.

3    the same (identical)     _____

In a distribution of deviation scores, the mean has a value of _____ .

5    0                        _____

When a raw score distribution is converted to a distribution of deviation scores, the variability (does/does not) change.

4    does not                 _____

Figure 7 is a histogram of the deviation scores for the group of boys who learned the finger maze. Their raw scores were 3, 7, 8, 8, 9, 9, 9, 9, 10, 11, 11, 14; their deviation scores were determined by subtracting the mean from each raw score.

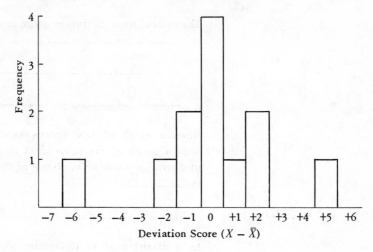

Fig. 7. Deviation scores of boys on a finger maze.

When the distribution of deviation scores for boys is compared with that for girls, which is shown again in Figure 8 below, it is evident that the two distributions differ in the manner in which the scores cluster about the mean.

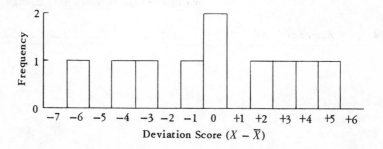

Fig. 8. Deviation scores of girls on a finger maze.

Figures 7 and 8 again make it clear that the range does not adequately describe the variability. Even if the ranges of two distributions are alike, there are many ways in which the scores can be distributed within the limits indicated by the range. A statistic is needed that will take into account all of the variability of scores in a distribution.

A deviation score is obtained by subtracting the_____ from the raw_____ .

1    mean                     _____

     score                    _____

If two distributions of measurements plotted on the same raw score scale differ in their variability, the same differences would be apparent on a_____ _____ scale.

2    deviation score          _____

It is possible for two distributions to have the same means and still differ in the way the scores cluster about their means.

3    true                     true_____false_____

If two distributions have the same range, they must have the same variability.

4    false                    true _____ false_____

1     As pointed out previously, a measure of variability will describe
a group of measurements better if it is based on every measurement
2     in the group. It is also useful to give special weight or importance
to those measurements that are the most unusual — that is, those
3     measurements farthest from the mean of the distribution. These
conditions for a method of describing variation have been met in a
4     statistic called the *variance*. The variance is defined as the mean
of the squares of the deviations of each measurement from the
mean. The formula for the variance ($s^2$) is:

5
$$s^2 = \frac{\Sigma(X - \overline{X})^2}{N} \, ,$$

where     $\overline{X}$ = the mean of the distribution of measures
     $X - \overline{X}$ = the difference between a single measurement and
          the mean of the measurements — that is, the devi-
          ation of a measurement from the mean
     $(X - \overline{X})^2$ = the square of each deviation score
     $\Sigma(X - \overline{X})^2$ = the sum of all the squared deviation scores
6          $N$ = the number of measures.

The variance includes all the data, because every measure in the
group is used in its computation. Special weight is given to the
extreme values because the deviation of each score is squared.
Another form of the formula for the variance is

7
$$s^2 = \frac{\Sigma x^2}{N} \, ,$$

where $x = (X - \overline{X})$. In this form of the formula, $x$ represents the
deviation of each measurement from the distribution mean.

The variability of a group of measurements is most adequately described if _____ measurement is used in determining it.

1  every

In computing the variance, the index point about which deviation values are computed is the _____.

4  mean

In the formula for the variance, those measures that are farthest from the mean are given more _____.

2  weight (importance)

The variance takes into account the mean, the weighted distance that scores are from the mean, and the _____ of subjects included in the group.

6  number

The fundamental statistic based on the weighted distance of scores from the mean and the number of subjects involved is known as the _____.

3  variance

The formula for determining the variance in a group of scores is $s^2 =$ _____.

5  $\dfrac{\Sigma(X - \bar{X})^2}{N}$, or

7  $\dfrac{\Sigma x^2}{N}$

To illustrate the method of calculating the variance we shall use an example. Suppose that the measurements listed in the score column below are the scores made by the ten girls mentioned before, who learned a finger maze. A score represents the number of trials required to learn the maze to the criterion of one perfect trial.

| | Subject | Score $(X)$ | $(X - \bar{X}) = x$ | $x^2$ |
|---|---|---|---|---|
| 1 | A | 14 | 5 | 25 |
| | B | 13 | 4 | 16 |
| | C | 12 | 3 | 9 |
| | D | 11 | 2 | 4 |
| | E | 9 | 0 | 0 |
| | F | 9 | 0 | 0 |
| | G | 8 | −1 | 1 |
| | H | 6 | −3 | 9 |
| | I | 5 | −4 | 16 |
| | J | 3 | −6 | 36 |
| 2,3 | $N = 10$ | $\Sigma X = 90$ | 0 | $\Sigma x^2 = 116$ |

The first step in finding the variance is to find the mean. The sum of the column of scores $(\Sigma X)$ is 90, the number of subjects is 10, so

4
$$\bar{X} = \frac{\Sigma X}{N} = \frac{90}{10} = 9 .$$

The mean is then subtracted from each girl's score; the resulting deviation scores are listed in the column headed $(X - \bar{X}) = x$. Each of the deviation scores is squared; these squares are listed in the column headed $x^2$. The $x^2$ column is added to obtain the sum of the squared deviation scores, $\Sigma x^2$. Finally, $\Sigma x^2$ is divided by $N$ to obtain the variance:

5
$$s^2 = \frac{\Sigma (X - \bar{X})^2}{N} = \frac{\Sigma x^2}{N} = \frac{116}{10} = 11.6 .$$

Note:  as a check of part of the work, $\Sigma (X - \bar{X})$ should equal zero.

A distribution of spelling test scores made by twelfth-grade boys is given below. Find the mean of the scores.

4    $\dfrac{440}{10} = 44$

$$\overline{X} = \frac{\Sigma \overline{X}}{N} = \underline{\hspace{2cm}}.$$

Complete the $(X - \overline{X})$ and the $x^2$ columns:

1

| $(X - \overline{X})$ | $x^2$ |
|---|---|
|  | 36 |
|  | 9 |
|  | 324 |
|  | 484 |
|  | 144 |
| −13 |  |
| 10 |  |
| 2 |  |
| −4 |  |
| 0 |  |

| Subject | Score $(X)$ | $(X - \overline{X})$ | $x^2$ |
|---|---|---|---|
| A | 38 | −6 | — |
| B | 47 | 3 | — |
| C | 62 | 18 | — |
| D | 22 | −22 | — |
| E | 56 | 12 | — |
| F | 31 | — | 169 |
| G | 54 | — | 100 |
| H | 46 | — | 4 |
| I | 40 | — | 16 |
| J | 44 | — | 0 |

Find $\Sigma(X - \overline{X})$.

2    0

Find $\Sigma x^2$.

3    1286

Find the variance:

5    128.6

$$s^2 = \frac{\Sigma x^2}{N} = \underline{\hspace{2cm}}.$$

Suppose we also calculate the variance of the scores made by the group of boys who learned the finger maze.

| | Subject | Score $(X)$ | $(X - \bar{X}) = x$ | $x^2$ |
|---|---|---|---|---|
| 1 | K | 14 | 5 | 25 |
| | L | 11 | 2 | 4 |
| | M | 11 | 2 | 4 |
| | N | 10 | 1 | 1 |
| | O | 9 | 0 | 0 |
| | P | 9 | 0 | 0 |
| | Q | 9 | 0 | 0 |
| | R | 9 | 0 | 0 |
| | S | 8 | −1 | 1 |
| | T | 8 | −1 | 1 |
| | U | 7 | −2 | 4 |
| | V | 3 | −6 | 36 |
| 2,3 | 12 | 108 | 0 | 76 |

$$\bar{X} = \frac{\Sigma X}{N} = \frac{108}{12} = 9.0.$$

4

$$s^2 = \frac{\Sigma(X - \bar{X})^2}{N} = \frac{\Sigma x^2}{N} = \frac{76}{12} = 6.3.$$

5

Having found the variance for these two groups, we can compare them. The girls' variance was 11.6 and the boys' variance was 6.3. We conclude that, among these particular boys and girls, the girls' scores are much more variable than the boys'. But this is true only for these boys and girls, not necessarily for boys and girls in general.

6

These examples show the desirable features in the formula for variance:

a. All the measurements are used to compute the variance.

b. Extra weight is given to measurements that are far from the mean by squaring all of the deviations.

c. Adjustment for the number of cases is made by dividing the sum of the squares of the deviations by $N$.

Below are the spelling test scores of a group of twelfth-grade girls. Find the mean of the scores.

4    $\dfrac{460}{10} = 46$

Complete the $x$ and $x^2$ columns:

| 1 | $x$ | $x^2$ | | Subject | Score $(X)$ | $x$ | $x^2$ |
|---|-----|-------|---|---------|-------------|-----|-------|
| | | 81 | | K | 37 | −9 | − |
| | | 9 | | L | 43 | −3 | − |
| | | 0 | | M | 46 | 0 | − |
| | | 324 | | N | 28 | −18 | − |
| | | 4 | | O | 48 | 2 | − |
| | 5 | | | P | 51 | − | 25 |
| | 1 | | | Q | 47 | − | 1 |
| | 17 | | | R | 63 | − | 289 |
| | −1 | | | S | 45 | − | 1 |
| | 6 | | | T | 52 | − | 36 |

2    0        $\Sigma x = \underline{\qquad}.$

3    770      $\Sigma x^2 = \underline{\qquad}.$

5    77.0     $s^2 = \dfrac{\Sigma x^2}{N} = \underline{\qquad}.$

In the problem on page 55, the variance of the twelfth-grade boys on the spelling test was 128.6. Can we say the twelfth-grade girls in general are more alike than all twelfth-grade boys in their spelling ability?

6    no (We don't know that these students are typical.)

1
2

3
4

The variance cannot easily be related to the original measures from which it was obtained. The reason for this is that all of the differences from the mean were squared. A measure of variability that is comparable to the original measures is obtained by taking the square root of the variance. The result is called the *standard deviation*. Because the standard deviation is the square root of particular squared measurements, it is expressed in the same units as the original measurements and hence can be compared with them.

The standard deviation is designated by the letter *s*. The formula for obtaining the standard deviation is:

5

$$s = \sqrt{s^2} = \sqrt{\frac{\Sigma(X - \bar{X})^2}{N}}$$

In Table 8 are shown the standard deviations of the groups we have used to demonstrate the method of obtaining the variance.

### Table 8
### Measures of Variability for Groups Learning a Finger Maze

| Groups | $s^2$ | $s = \sqrt{s^2}$ |
|--------|-------|------------------|
| Girls  | 11.6  | 3.4 trials       |
| Boys   | 6.3   | 2.5 trials       |

6

The standard deviation of the girls' scores is almost one trial more than the standard deviation of the boys' scores. This, in standard deviation terms, again indicates a difference in variability between the groups.

The variance is the mean of the sum of the _____ deviations of each score from the mean.

1    squared

_____

A measure of variability that can be compared with the original scores is obtained by taking the _____ _____ of the variance.

2    square root

_____

The square root of the variance is known as the _____ _____ .

3    standard deviation

_____

If the original measures in an experiment are expressed in millimeters, the standard deviation would be expressed in _____ .

4    millimeters

_____

5    $\sqrt{\dfrac{\Sigma(X - \overline{X})^2}{N}}$

The formula for the standard deviation is

$$s = \sqrt{s^2} = \underline{\hspace{2cm}}.$$

The relative size of the standard deviations in two groups of measurements indicates the relative amount of _____ in the two groups.

6    variability

_____

# Chapter 5

# THE NORMAL DISTRIBUTION CURVE

1

2

3

The standard deviation is the accepted statistic for describing variability. A detailed explanation of the reasons for this can not be given here, but a rough explanation is possible. It has been noted that measurements of many kinds of behavior tend to be distributed symmetrically and to cluster about the mean. Much theoretical and experimental investigation has shown that there is a typical behavior distribution which can be expressed mathematically. This distribution is called the normal probability distribution or just the *normal distribution*.

4

Figure 9 is a histogram representing a hypothetical distribution of measurements of the behavior of a large group of subjects. The smooth curve superimposed on the histogram is a normal distribution curve.

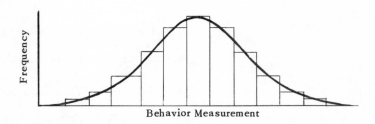

Fig. 9. A normal distribution.

5

The smooth curve may be thought of as connecting the mid-points of the tops of the bars of a histogram that reports results from a very large group of experimental subjects. Of course, when the number of subjects is small the histogram is seldom so regular. Hence, the normal distribution curve is considered an ideal curve — that is, the more subjects used, the more closely the data usually fit the normal curve.

The statistic usually employed to describe the variability in a group of measurements is known as the _____ _____.

1    standard deviation    _____

Measurements of many kinds of behavior tend to be_____ symmetrically.

2    distributed    _____

The curve that is most used to represent the distribution of behavior in groups is known as the_____ _____curve.

3    normal distribution    _____

In psychology, the horizontal scale on the normal curve usually represents measurements of some kind of_____.

4    behavior    _____

The smooth normal curve is approximately the curve we would expect if we connected the mid-points of the tops of the bars of a _____.

5    histogram    _____

1    The normal distribution curve represents a smoothed normal histogram, and the area between the curve and the horizontal axis repre-
2    sents all of the measurements in any distribution. This is the case
whether the distribution contains only a few, several hundred, or
several thousand measurements. It is useful, therefore, to deal with
areas under the curve in terms of percentages rather than in terms
of any specific $N$. The percentage of the area under the curve between any pair of scores or between the mean and a score, expressed
in standard deviations, can be determined readily from tables that
are available in most standard statistics texts. Certain important
areas are given here, and illustrated in the figure below:

3    About 68 per cent of all the scores are within ±1$s$ of the mean.

About 95 per cent of all the scores are within ±2$s$ of the mean.

4    Almost, but not quite, 100 per cent (actually, about 99.7 per cent)
of all the scores are within ±3$s$ of the mean.

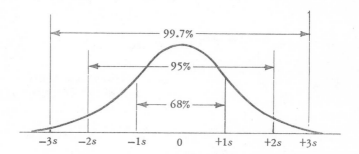

Fig. 10. Percentages of area under the normal curve within specified
standard deviations from the mean.

The area between the normal curve and the horizontal axis includes_____of the behavior measurements taken of a group of subjects.

1    all

_____

The area under the normal curve represents all of the cases in a group no matter how _____the group is.

2    large

_____

Approximately two-thirds (68 per cent) of the scores in a normal distribution lie within_____standard deviations of the mean.

3    one (±1)

_____

Between −3$s$ and +3$s$, in a normal distribution, will be found almost_____per cent of the scores.

4    100

_____

The normal probability distribution and its graph, the normal curve, have many important applications in statistics. Thus it is necessary to know certain constant characteristics of this model distribution. The mean divides the distribution into symmetrical halves, each of which includes 50 per cent or half of the measures. (Therefore, you may notice, the median and the mean are the same when the distribution is normal.) The area between the mean and the point one standard deviation *above* the mean includes approximately one-third of the measures, about 34 per cent. The same proportion of the measures is included between the mean and the point one standard deviation *below* the mean. Thus, between the two points that are one standard deviation away from the mean — that is, between ±1s — are included approximately two-thirds of the measures, about 68 per cent.

Between ±1.96s are included 95 per cent of the measures. In each extremity or tail of the curve beyond ±1.96s are 2.5 per cent of the measures.

Between ±2.58s are included 99 per cent of the measures. Only 1 per cent of the total measures deviate from the mean, above or below, by as much or more than 2.58s. The values 1.96 and 2.58 are particularly critical values for later applications.

These relationships are illustrated in Figure 11.

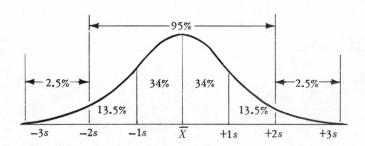

Fig. 11. The normal distribution curve.

The normal curve represents a distribution that is dispersed symmetrically about the _____.

1    mean

In a normal distribution, _____ per cent of the measures lie above the mean.

2    50

A score $1s$ above the mean of a normal distribution would be higher than about 84 per cent of all the scores; that is, it would exceed the 50 per cent of scores below the mean and the _____ per cent between the mean and $+1s$.

3    34

A score that is $1s$ below the mean of a normal distribution would exceed approximately _____ per cent of all the scores.

4    16

Because 95 per cent of all the measures in a normal distribution lie between $\pm 1.96s$, the extreme high and low scores which are below $-1.96s$ and above $+1.96s$ represent only _____ per cent of all the measures.

5    5

The most commonly used unit of variability is the standard deviation. References to the normal curve are almost always made in
terms of numbers of standard deviations. Measurements, on the
other hand, are frequently reported in such units as time, trials,
or percentage. Usually these various measurement units can not
be compared directly. If a student had a test score of 60 on a
psychology test and a score of 9 on a mathematics test, we would
not be able to compare the scores without a common yardstick.
When the scores are converted to standard deviation units, the
standard deviation becomes the common yardstick, and such comparisons can be made. Such converted scores are called *standard
scores* or *z* scores. The formula for converting a raw score to a
standard score is:

$$z = \frac{X - \overline{X}}{s},$$

where $z$ = the standard score that is to be found
$X$ = the raw score
$\overline{X}$ = the mean of the distribution of scores
$s$ = the standard deviation of the distribution.

Now let us apply this formula to the scores of the student mentioned above. If the mean of the scores on the psychology test was
55 and the *s* was 5, a raw score of 60 would be equivalent to a *z*
score of +1:

$$z = \frac{X - \overline{X}}{s} = \frac{60 - 55}{5} = \frac{5}{5} = 1.$$

If the mean of the test scores from the mathematics test was 6 and
the *s* was 1.5, the student's raw score of 9 would be represented
by a *z* score of 2:

$$z = \frac{X - \overline{X}}{s} = \frac{9 - 6}{1.5} = \frac{3}{1.5} = 2.$$

This student, then, exceeded the mean performance of his psychology class by one standard deviation, and exceeded the mean
performance of his mathematics class by two standard deviations.
His superiority, relative to the performance of others in the classes,
was greater in mathematics – in spite of the numerical values of the
raw scores.

An individual's performances on two different tests can be compared when his raw
scores are converted to_____scores.

1    standard ($z$)    _____

A student received a score of 75 on an
English test. The mean of the class was
69, the standard deviation 12. What standard
score did the student get?

2    0.5    $$z = \frac{X - \bar{X}}{s} = \text{_____}.$$

The same student received a score of 93 on
a biology test. The class mean was 90, the
standard deviation was 3. What was his $z$
score on the biology test?

3    1.0    _____

On which test did he have the better score
when compared with his class?

4    The biology test.    _____

In the finger maze experiment described in Chapter 4, the slowest learning score among the boys was 14 trials. (The more trials taken, the slower the learning.) The slowest learning score for girls was also 14 trials. The boy and girl with scores of 14 were not equal in slowness, however, when compared with members of their own sex. Among the girls, 14 trials was 5 trials longer than average. The standard deviation of the girls' scores was 3.4. Thus the slowest girl's z score is 5/3.4 = 1.5. That is, the score of 14 is 1.5 standard deviations above the mean performance of the girls. The standard score of the boy who took 5 trials more than average was 5/2.5 = 2.0; his score was 2 standard deviations above the mean performance of the boys. Thus the boy was somewhat slower, in comparison to his sex group, than was the girl, in comparison to her sex group. Remember that the more trials the subject takes, the slower the learning. Hence a low raw score and a negative standard score reflect superior performance in this case.

1     The standard score may be defined as the quotient obtained when an individual's deviation score is divided by the standard deviation. The formula is repeated here:

2,3
$$z = \frac{X - \overline{X}}{s}.$$

Another form of the formula is

$$z = \frac{x}{s}.$$

4
5     A standard score is the number of standard deviations the raw score is from the mean. If the raw score is *below* the mean, the standard score will be *negative*.

To find out how many standard deviations from the mean a given score lies, one divides $(X - \overline{X})$ by _____.

1     $s$

---

The symbol used to designate a standard score is the letter _____.

2     $z$

---

An individual has a raw score of 89. If $\overline{X} = 104$ and $s = 10$, his standard score is _____.

3     −1.5

---

The number of standard deviations between a measurement and the mean is called the _____ score.

4     standard

---

The standard score of an individual whose raw score is below the mean will always be _____.

5     negative

---

The raw scores and $z$ scores of the students in the maze learning experiment are presented in Table 9.

Table 9

Raw Scores and Standard Scores for the Finger Maze Experiment

| Subject (girls) | Raw score (trials) | Standard score | Subject (boys) | Raw score (trials) | Standard score |
|---|---|---|---|---|---|
| A | 14 | 1.5 | K | 14 | 2.0 |
| B | 13 | 1.1 | L | 11 | 0.8 |
| C | 12 | 0.9 | M | 11 | 0.8 |
| D | 11 | 0.6 | N | 10 | 0.4 |
| E | 9 | 0.0 | O | 9 | 0.0 |
| F | 9 | 0.0 | P | 9 | 0.0 |
| G | 8 | −0.3 | Q | 9 | 0.0 |
| H | 6 | −0.9 | R | 9 | 0.0 |
| I | 5 | −1.1 | S | 8 | −0.4 |
| J | 3 | −1.7 | T | 8 | −0.4 |
|   |   |   | U | 7 | −0.8 |
|   |   |   | V | 3 | −2.4 |

1
2

3
4
Because the boys, as a group, vary less in their performance than the girls, a boy who has the same raw score as a girl will have a larger $z$ score. We have seen that although subjects A and K both had raw scores of 14, the boy's $z$ score was 2.0 and the girl's score was 1.5. Similarly, subjects J and V both had raw scores of 3, but the boy's $z$ score was −2.4 while the girl's was −1.7.

5
The standard deviation lets us compare the overall variability in one group with the overall variability in another. The standard score, which is obtained from the standard deviation, lets us compare the performance of individuals in one group with the performance of individuals in another, not in terms of raw score but in terms of their relative performance as compared with others in their own groups.

In the maze learning experiment, girl H has a negative *z* score because she required _____trials than average to learn the maze.

1    fewer    _____

If a person has a standard score of 0, it is because his performance is exactly the same as the_____performance of his group.

2    mean (average)    _____

Two people in different groups whose performance has been measured on the same task can have different standard scores even though their raw scores are the same.

4    true    true_____ false_____

Two people in different groups whose performance has been measured on the same task can not have the same standard scores unless they have the same raw scores.

3    false    true_____ false_____

Determine the *z* score in the two cases below. Which individual did better in comparison with others in his own group?

| | Raw score | $\bar{X}$ | s | z |
|---|---|---|---|---|
| Mary | 75 | 65 | 10 | _____ |
| Jack | 70 | 60 | 7 | _____ |

5    1
     1.43

     Jack    _____

Chapter 6

# CORRELATION

1      Measures of central tendency and variability are useful tools in describing a distribution of values of a single variable such as reaction time or intelligence. They do not, however, tell anything about the possible relationship between two or more such variables.

2 When the relationship between two or more variables is investi-
3 gated, a multivariate analysis is used. We will consider only a
4 bivariate analysis, which deals with two variables. An essential feature of the bivariate method is that the observations or measures for each subject or condition are paired.

It is often desirable to know the degree to which certain traits or abilities are related. For example, a psychometrist might wish to determine the relationship between the scholastic-aptitude test scores and the grade-point averages received by certain students. To do this, he would need measures of both variables for each student in the group being considered. One measure would be the student's score on the aptitude test, the other his grade-point average. From these scores it is possible to determine a number which represents the degree of relationship between the variables in the group of students being considered. This number may vary in value
5 from +1 through 0 to −1. Either a +1 or −1 indicates a maximum
6 relationship. Zero indicates that the variables are not related. Numbers between +1 and 0 and between −1 and 0 indicate inter- mediate degrees of relatedness.

The statistical methods thus far considered are used to describe distributions of values of a _____ variable.

1    single

When the relationship between two or more variables is investigated, a _____ analysis is used.

2    multivariate

A bivariate analysis indicates the relationship between _____ variables.

3    two

Observations used in a bivariate analysis are always present in _____.

4    pairs

A maximum relationship is indicated by the numbers _____ and _____.

5    +1

      −1

A lack of relationship between two variables is indicated by the number _____.

6    0

1
2
3

The number which indicates degree of relatedness is called a *correlation coefficient*. The most commonly used correlation coefficient is the Pearson product-moment coefficient of correlation, which is symbolized by $r$.

Before the product-moment method is described, let us examine the basic idea of bivariate analyses. Initially there are pairs of test scores or other measures for each subject in our group. These scores might be represented in a table as follows:

### Table 10
#### Symbolic Representation of Subjects' Scores on Test X and Test Y

| Subject | Score on Test X | Score on Test Y |
|---------|-----------------|-----------------|
| $A_1$ | $X_1$ | $Y_1$ |
| $A_2$ | $X_2$ | $Y_2$ |
| $A_3$ | $X_3$ | $Y_3$ |
| . | . | . |
| . | . | . |
| . | . | . |
| $A_n$ | $X_n$ | $Y_n$ |

4

In this table, the test score $X_1$ and the test score $Y_1$ were the scores received by individual $A_1$. Each subject in the group ($A_1$, $A_2$, $A_3$, ... $A_n$) has a score on both test X and test Y. The numerical subscripts identify the subject with the test scores he received.

The statistic which indicates the degree of relatedness between two variables is the_____ of correlation.

1    coefficient                    _____

The Pearson product-moment coefficient of _____ is the most commonly used measure of relatedness.

2    correlation                    _____

In order to find the relationship between test X and test Y in a group of subjects, the subjects must have a _____ on both tests.

4    score                          _____

The symbol for the Pearson product-moment coefficient of correlation is_____ .

3    *r*                            _____

1    An earlier chapter demonstrated the graphic method in which scores
on a single variable are represented on the horizontal axis and the
2    frequency of these scores is represented on the vertical axis. In
the graph used to illustrate correlation, the scores of one of the
variables are represented on the abscissa, the scores of the second
variable on the ordinate.

3    Each pair of values is plotted by finding the point representing
both the $X$ and $Y$ values. This is accomplished by locating the $X$
value of a pair of measures on the horizontal axis and the $Y$ value
on the vertical axis. The required point is located directly above
the $X$ value and opposite the $Y$ value at the point where two lines
perpendicular to the axes, one at $X$ and one at $Y$, would intersect.
Each pair of values in the distribution can be so plotted. The point
$(X_1, Y_1)$ represents the $X$ and $Y$ values for the first subject, $(X_2,
Y_2)$ the $X$ and $Y$ values for the second subject, and so on. An ex-
ample of such a graph is shown below.

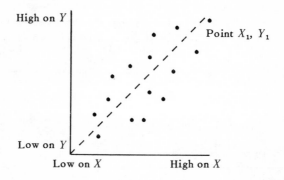

Fig. 12. Graphic representation of a high positive correlation.

4    In this arrangement a person who scores high on test X will typically score high on test Y. A person with a low score on test X
will typically have a low score on test Y. This arrangement repre-
5    sents a high *positive* relationship. When two measures are highly
related, the plotted points tend to be on a straight line as shown
in Figure 12.

In a histogram or frequency polygon, the values of the variable are represented on the_____ axis.

1  horizontal *(X)*

_____

When the values of a variable are plotted on the horizontal axis, and the values of a second variable are plotted on the vertical axis,_____ is being illustrated.

2  correlation

_____

When a pair of scores for a subject is plotted on a graph, both the $X$ and $Y$ values are plotted at a _____ point.

3  single (common)

_____

When each subject who scores high on the $X$ variable also scores high on the $Y$ variable, and each subject who scores low on the $X$ variable scores low on the $Y$ variable, there is a high_____relationship between the variables.

4  positive

_____

In a graph showing a high positive relationship, the plotted points tend to lie on a _____ _____.

5  straight line

_____

1   The hypothetical arrangement in Figure 13 represents a lack of any
relationship between variables $X$ and $Y$. Thus a person who scores
high on test X might have a high, medium, or low score on test Y.
This means that knowing a subject's score on test X would not
help us predict his score on test Y.

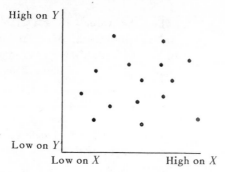

Fig. 13. Graphic representation of a minimal relationship.

Figure 14 represents a high *negative* correlation. In such a case,
a person who scores high on test X will typically score low on
test Y.

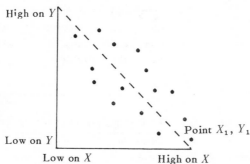

Fig. 14. Graphic representation of a high negative relationship.

2   A graph of plotted pairs of test scores is called a scatter diagram.
3   Such diagrams illustrate the relationship between two variables.
4   The more nearly the plotted points fall on a straight line cutting
the graph diagonally, the greater the correlation between the vari-
5   ables. If the line slopes upward (as it moves to the right), the
correlation is positive; if it slopes downward, as it does in Figure
14, the correlation is negative. The greater the scatter of points,
the lower is the represented correlation.

If a high score on one variable may be paired with a high, average, or low score on the second variable, then the degree of relationship between the two variables is _____ .

1    minimal (0)

A graph of paired test scores is known as a _____ diagram.

2    scatter

Scatter diagrams illustrate the _____ between two variables, $X$ and $Y$.

3    relationship

When two variables are highly correlated, the points in their scatter diagram tend to lie in a _____ _____ .

4    straight line

When there is a relationship between two plotted variables, the points in the scatter diagram tend to lie in a straight line. The slope of this line indicates whether the correlation is _____ or _____ .

5    positive

     negative

The formula for computing the Pearson product-moment coefficient of correlation, $r$, is:

$$r = \frac{\Sigma xy}{N s_x s_y} \, ,$$

where $r$ = the index number indicating the degree of relatedness between $X$ and $Y$

1

$x$ = the deviation of an $X$ score from the mean of all the $X$ scores, $(X - \bar{X})$

$y$ = the deviation of a $Y$ score from the mean of all the $Y$ scores, $(Y - \bar{Y})$

$\Sigma xy$ = the sum of the products of the deviation scores of each pair of measures

$s_x$ = the standard deviation of the $X$ distribution

2

$s_y$ = the standard deviation of the $Y$ distribution

3

$N$ = the number of subjects in the group.

4

As the size of the sample increases, a coefficient of correlation becomes difficult to compute. As a result, when $N$ is large or when several correlation coefficients are to be determined it is practical to use a calculating machine or a computer. When the sample of subjects is small the coefficient of correlation is easily computed from this formula.

In the formula

$$r = \frac{\Sigma xy}{N s_x s_y},$$

$x$ = the deviation of an $X$ score from the _____ of the $X$ scores.

1    mean

In the formula above, $s_y$ = the standard deviation of the $Y$_____ .

2    distribution (scores)

In the formula above, $N$ = the_____of subjects in the group.

3    number

A calculating machine or computer is usually used to determine a correlation coefficient when the sample is_____.

4    large

The computation of a Pearson product-moment coefficient of correlation for a hypothetical distribution of five pairs of scores is shown below:

| Subject | Test X | Test Y | $x$ | $y$ | $x^2$ | $y^2$ | $xy$ |
|---------|--------|--------|-----|-----|-------|-------|------|
| A | 50 | 10 | 20 | −20 | 400 | 400 | −400 |
| B | 40 | 20 | 10 | −10 | 100 | 100 | −100 |
| C | 30 | 30 | 0 | 0 | 0 | 0 | 0 |
| D | 20 | 40 | −10 | 10 | 100 | 100 | −100 |
| E | 10 | 50 | −20 | 20 | 400 | 400 | −400 |
|   | 150 | 150 | 0 | 0 | 1000 | 1000 | −1000 |

1
$$\bar{X} = \frac{\Sigma X}{N} = \frac{150}{5} = 30.$$

2
$$\bar{Y} = \frac{\Sigma Y}{N} = \frac{150}{5} = 30.$$

3
$$s_x = \sqrt{\frac{\Sigma x^2}{N}} = \sqrt{\frac{1000}{5}} = \sqrt{200} = 14.14.$$

4
$$s_y = \sqrt{\frac{\Sigma y^2}{N}} = \sqrt{\frac{1000}{5}} = \sqrt{200} = 14.14.$$

Substituting these values in the formula for the correlation coefficient:

5
$$r = \frac{\Sigma xy}{N s_x s_y} = \frac{-1000}{5(14.14)(14.14)} = \frac{-1000}{1000} = -1.00.$$

This is an example of a maximum negative relationship since the value for $r$ is −1.00. If the order of the scores on test Y had been reversed, that is, if the $X$ and $Y$ scores had been identical, the resulting coefficient of correlation would have been +1.00. This would represent a maximum positive relationship.

Given the following hypothetical distribution of pairs of scores:

| Subject | $X$ | $Y$ | $x$ | $y$ | $x^2$ | $y^2$ | $xy$ |
|---------|-----|-----|-----|-----|-------|-------|------|
| A | 50 | 50 | 20 | 20 | 400 | 400 | 400 |
| B | 40 | 40 | 10 | 10 | 100 | 100 | 100 |
| C | 30 | 30 | 0 | 0 | 0 | 0 | 0 |
| D | 20 | 20 | −10 | −10 | 100 | 100 | 100 |
| E | 10 | 10 | −20 | −20 | 400 | 400 | 400 |
| | 150 | 150 | 0 | 0 | 1000 | 1000 | 1000 |

1    30
$$\bar{X} = \frac{\Sigma X}{N} = \underline{\qquad}.$$

2    30
$$\bar{Y} = \frac{\Sigma Y}{N} = \underline{\qquad}.$$

3    14.14
$$s_x = \sqrt{\frac{\Sigma x^2}{N}} = \underline{\qquad}.$$

4    14.14
$$s_y = \sqrt{\frac{\Sigma y^2}{N}} = \underline{\qquad}.$$

5    1.00
$$r = \frac{\Sigma xy}{N s_x s_y} = \frac{1000}{5(14.14)(14.14)} = \underline{\qquad}.$$

Correlations of ±1 are seldom found in psychological studies. This is because of our inability to control all the factors that influence our measurements. If, for example, scores on a test of college aptitude were compared with the average grade received in the first semester of college, it would be impossible to include all the pertinent factors in the study. The motivation of the subjects could not be held constant nor could every student take the same classes at the same time of day from the same instructor. These are but a few of the uncontrolled conditions which might influence the measures. The net result is that correlation coefficients usually fall in the range between +1 and −1.

Computation of the correlation coefficient for the scores on two successive psychology examinations is shown in the following example. Scores on the first examination are denoted by $X$, those on the second examination by $Y$.

| Student | $X$ | $Y$ | $x$ | $y$ | $x^2$ | $y^2$ | $xy$ |
|---------|-----|-----|-----|-----|-------|-------|------|
| 1 | 80 | 81 | 9 | 7 | 81 | 49 | 63 |
| 2 | 81 | 80 | 10 | 6 | 100 | 36 | 60 |
| 3 | 66 | 74 | −5 | 0 | 25 | 0 | 0 |
| 4 | 62 | 60 | −9 | −14 | 81 | 196 | 126 |
| 5 | 75 | 72 | 4 | −2 | 16 | 4 | −8 |
| 6 | 62 | 77 | −9 | 3 | 81 | 9 | −27 |
|   | 426 | 444 | 0 | 0 | 384 | 294 | 214 |

1
$$\bar{X} = \frac{\Sigma X}{N} = \frac{426}{6} = 71.0.$$

2
$$\bar{Y} = \frac{\Sigma Y}{N} = \frac{444}{6} = 74.0.$$

3
$$s_x = \sqrt{\frac{\Sigma x^2}{N}} = \sqrt{\frac{384}{6}} = \sqrt{64} = 8.0.$$

4
$$s_y = \sqrt{\frac{\Sigma y^2}{N}} = \sqrt{\frac{294}{6}} = \sqrt{49} = 7.0.$$

5
$$r = \frac{\Sigma xy}{N s_x s_y} = \frac{214}{6(8)(7)} = \frac{214}{336} = .64.$$

Given the test scores of six students on two tests in General Psychology, with scores on the first test denoted by $X$, scores on the second denoted by $Y$:

| Student | $X$ | $Y$ | $x$ | $y$ | $x^2$ | $y^2$ | $xy$ |
|---|---|---|---|---|---|---|---|
| 1 | 81 | 80 | 10 | 6 | 100 | 36 | 60 |
| 2 | 75 | 81 | 4 | 7 | 16 | 49 | 28 |
| 3 | 62 | 60 | -9 | -14 | 81 | 196 | 126 |
| 4 | 66 | 74 | -5 | 0 | 25 | 0 | 0 |
| 5 | 80 | 77 | 9 | 3 | 81 | 9 | 27 |
| 6 | 62 | 72 | -9 | -2 | 81 | 4 | 18 |
| | 426 | 444 | 0 | 0 | 384 | 294 | 259 |

1     71

$$\bar{X} = \frac{\Sigma X}{N} = \underline{\hspace{2cm}}.$$

2     74

$$\bar{Y} = \frac{\Sigma Y}{N} = \underline{\hspace{2cm}}.$$

3     8

$$s_x = \sqrt{\frac{\Sigma x^2}{N}} = \underline{\hspace{2cm}}.$$

4     7

$$s_y = \sqrt{\frac{\Sigma y^2}{N}} = \underline{\hspace{2cm}}.$$

5     .77

$$r = \frac{\Sigma xy}{N s_x s_y} = \frac{259}{6(8)(7)} = \underline{\hspace{2cm}}.$$

1     When the characteristics of the distribution of a population on a single variable are known, a prediction of the value of a measure for any member of the population can be made. This prediction is better than just a guess. It is the most typical value in the distribution. In most applications, this would be the population mean.

2     If two variables are related, and we know an individual's position on one variable, we are able to make a better prediction of his position on the second variable. This is particularly valuable when the predictor variable is easy to measure, or when the variable to be predicted depends upon future performance over an extended period of time. An example is the prediction of college success by means of an aptitude test score. The aptitude test is easy to administer and the grade-point average which represents the degree of success in college requires many months or years to be determined. If the scores on variables $X$ and $Y$ are correlated, the $Y$ score a subject is likely to obtain can be predicted if his $X$ score is known. The greater the value of the correlation coefficient, the

3     more accurate the prediction will be. An $r$ of 1.00 provides a perfect prediction of a $Y$ score, given an $X$ score.

4     Two precautions must be taken when interpreting a coefficient of correlation. First, the range of values of a coefficient of correlation does not form a scale of equal units. That is, an $r$ of .5 does not indicate half the predictive efficiency of an $r$ of 1.00. Second, two measures that are correlated are not necessarily causally related. Both variables may be influenced by a third variable. Even when there is a causal relationship involved, $r$ does not in itself indicate which is cause and which is effect.

If Jim is an adult American male and the average (mean) height of adult American males is 5 feet 9 inches, what height would we predict for Jim?

1    5 feet 9 inches

    —————————————————

Suppose that the average weight of adult American males is 155 pounds, and suppose also that height and weight are positively correlated. If we know Jim is 4 inches taller than average, we would predict that he weighs———————than 155 pounds.

2    more

    —————————————————

To make a perfectly accurate prediction of an individual's position on one variable from knowledge of his position on a second variable, the coefficient of correlation between the variables must be —————.

3    1.00

    —————————————————

Two variables may not be causally related yet they may be—————.

4    correlated

    —————————————————

# Chapter 7

# INTRODUCTION TO PROBABILITY

1

2

The earlier lessons have been primarily concerned with methods for describing, in as brief and meaningful a fashion as possible, outcomes that have already been observed. This *descriptive* function is an important application of statistical tools. But beyond description, the psychologist wishes to make predictions and generalizations from his observations. To understand the methods he uses it is necessary to consider some basic principles of *probability*.

3

Probability is a familiar concept in our everyday lives. Probabilities are often referred to as "chances" or "odds." When predicting the sex of an expected child, for example, we say the chances are about "fifty-fifty" that it will be a boy. We may predict the outcome of some event by saying that the odds are 2 to 1, or that they are 10 to 1. Such statements are statements of probability. Through everyday use, you have gained at least a sketchy familiarity with the principles of probability.

4

5

The first step in considering probability formally is to establish a numerical representation of probability. If it can be stated with absolute certainty that an outcome will occur, the probability of that outcome is represented by the number 1. An outcome that absolutely will not occur has a probability represented by the number 0. Any intermediate probability is represented by some value between 1 and 0.

When we speak of the "odds" or "chances" of a given outcome, we are referring to the _____ of that outcome.

3    probability    _____

The probability of an outcome that is absolutely certain to occur is represented by the number_____ .

4    1    _____

If an outcome may or may not occur, its probability is represented by a number between_____ and_____ .

5    1    _____

   0    _____

Statistics which are used to describe outcomes that have already been observed are called_____statistics.

1    descriptive    _____

When a psychologist uses his observations to make predictions about future events, he must apply the principles of_____ .

2    probability    _____

*Mutually exclusive outcomes* are outcomes that can not occur at the same time. For example, a coin that lands with a head showing can not also have a tail showing. If a die lands with three spots showing on the top face, no other result is possible at the same time.

1    When a coin is flipped, it can be stated with absolute assurance that the probability of either a head or tail resulting (excluding the highly improbable outcome of its standing on edge) is 1. If the coin is unbiased, the probability that it will land heads is equal to the probability that it will land tails, so the probability of each of these outcomes is 1/2. The sum of the mutually exclusive probabilities is 1/2 + 1/2 = 1. Whenever the probabilities of all possible outcomes of an event are totalled, their sum is equal to 1.

2    As an example, suppose an unbiased die is cast. The possible out-
3    comes are 1, 2, 3, 4, 5, 6. Since each outcome is equally probable, the probability of a 1 resulting is 1/6, the probability of a 2 resulting is 1/6, and so on through 6. The sum of the probabilities of the mutually exclusive outcomes is:

$$\frac{1}{6} + \frac{1}{6} + \frac{1}{6} + \frac{1}{6} + \frac{1}{6} + \frac{1}{6} = 1.$$

We may summarize these facts in three rules:

4    a.  If an outcome is certain to occur, its probability is 1; if it is certain not to occur, its probability is 0.

5    b.  If there are $n$ possible outcomes of an event, and the outcomes are mutually exclusive and equally probable, the probability of any one outcome occurring is $1/n$.

c.  The probability that some member of a set of mutually exclusive outcomes will occur is equal to the sum of the probabilities of each outcome in the set.

A coin with a head on both sides is flipped. Since only a head is possible, the probability of a head appearing on the toss is _____ .

4          1

A coin that has an equal probability of a head or a tail resulting from a flip is called an _____ coin.

1          unbiased

If a single unbiased die with six faces is cast, the probability of obtaining a 4 is _____ .

3          $\frac{1}{6}$

"The probability that one of $n$ mutually exclusive but equally probable outcomes will occur is $1/n$." When this rule is applied to the case of tossing a die, $n$ is equal to _____ .

2          6

If the numbers 1 through 8 are placed in a hat and one number is drawn, and if each number has an equal chance of being drawn, the probability that the number 5 will be drawn is _____ .

5          $\frac{1}{8}$

Outcomes are seldom considered in isolation. In playing dice, matching coins, or performing experiments, outcomes occurring together are often considered. The probability that two or more outcomes will occur jointly is determined by combining the probabilities of the single events according to the following rule.

1
2    When two or more independent outcomes may occur jointly, the probability of their joint occurrence is equal to the *product* of the probabilities of the outcomes treated independently.

Suppose two pennies are flipped at the same time. A head (H) on one coin could be paired with either a head (HH) or tail (HT) on the second coin. A tail on the first coin could yield either (TH) or (TT).

3    The result (HH) is a joint outcome, so its probability is equal to the probability of the first coin landing heads (1/2), times the probability that the second coin will land heads (1/2). The probability of (HH), then, is $1/2 \cdot 1/2 = 1/4$. The same is true of (TT), (HT), and (TH). The outcomes (HT) and (TH) are essentially the same. The result in either case is one head and one tail, and it does not matter much which coin is which. So the probabilities of these two outcomes are usually summed: the probability of one head and one tail is $1/4 + 1/4 = 1/2$.

A pair of dice is cast. The probability that both faces will show the number 6 is _____.

1  $\dfrac{1}{6} \cdot \dfrac{1}{6} = \dfrac{1}{36}$

_____

The multiplicative rule deals with outcomes occurring jointly. The probability of a joint outcome is equal to the _____ of the independent probabilities of the individual outcomes.

2  product

_____

If we wish to determine the probability that casting two dice will result in a 3 and a 4, we would determine the probability of a 3 on the first die and a 4 on the second, and the probability of a 4 on the first die and a 3 on the second, and then find the _____ of these two probabilities.

3  sum

_____

1     A histogram of the distribution of possible outcomes resulting from flipping two coins is shown below:

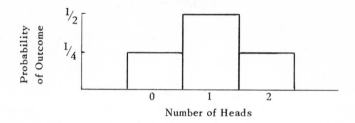

2     Fig. 15. Probability of outcomes of a toss of two coins.

3     If the example is expanded to include four coins, there are 16 possible outcomes:

| TTTT | HTTT | HHTT | HHHT | HHHH |
|------|------|------|------|------|
|      | THTT | HTHT | HHTH |      |
|      | TTHT | HTTH | HTHH |      |
|      | TTTH | TTHH | THHH |      |
|      |      | THTH |      |      |
|      |      | THHT |      |      |

The total number of equally likely outcomes is 16, so each has a probability of 1/16. There are four ways to get a result of three heads and one tail; adding their probabilities gives a *combined* probability of 4/16 or 1/4. In like manner, the probability of two heads is 6/16, the probability of one head is 4/16, and the probability of no heads is 1/16. A histogram of this distribution is shown in Figure 16.

4

5

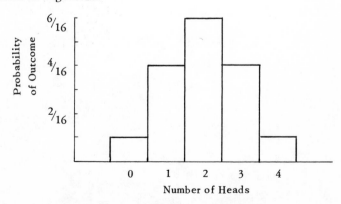

Fig. 16. Probability of outcomes of a toss of four coins.

When two or more possible outcomes are essentially the same, their individual probabilities are often added to give their_____ probability.

4  combined

_____

Two coins are tossed. The probability that both will land heads, plus the probability that both will land tails, equals the probability that their faces will match. Thus the probability that their faces will match is_____ .

1  $\frac{1}{4} + \frac{1}{4} = \frac{1}{2}$

_____

When several coins are flipped, the probability is high that the number of heads and the number of tails will be approximately _____ .

5  equal

_____

If two coins are flipped on four occasions, the faces would be expected to match on _____ of the occasions.

2  two (half)

_____

As the size of the sample of coins that are flipped increases, the number of possible outcomes_____ .

3  increases

_____

1
2

The probability distributions for both two and four coins show that the probability of an equal number of heads and tails on any trial is greater than the probability of any other single outcome. The extreme cases, such as all heads or all tails, are least probable.

An extension of these examples is the six-coin distribution presented in Figure 17. The number of possible outcomes is greater, but the distribution has the same characteristic shape as those for fewer coins.

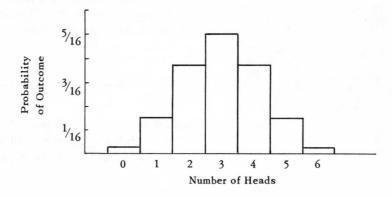

3,4    Fig. 17. Probability of outcomes of a toss of six coins.

In this example the theoretical probability of six heads is

$$\frac{1}{2} \cdot \frac{1}{2} \cdot \frac{1}{2} \cdot \frac{1}{2} \cdot \frac{1}{2} \cdot \frac{1}{2} = \frac{1}{64}.$$

5

Another way of expressing this probability is to say that if six coins were to be flipped 64 times, six heads would be expected on only 1 flip. In like manner, five heads would be expected on 6 flips, four heads on 15 flips, three heads on 20 flips, two heads on 15 flips, one head on 6 flips, and no heads on 1 flip.

When four coins are flipped, an outcome of four heads is_____ likely than an outcome of two heads and two tails.

1   less

When six coins are flipped, the probability of five heads and one tail is (less than/equal to/greater than) the probability of one head and five tails.

4   equal to

Six coins are flipped. The probability of three heads and three tails is_____ than the probability of four heads and two tails.

3   greater

When four coins are tossed, the most likely outcome, according to a theoretical probability model, would be_____heads.

2   two

The probability that an equal number of heads and tails will result from a toss of six coins is 5/16. This result is more likely than any other single combination of heads and tails. However, the probability that the number of heads and tails will not be the same is_____than the probability that they will be equal.

5   greater

The distributions of possible outcomes were determined by applying the mathematical rules of probability. If coins were actually tossed, it is likely that the result would not agree exactly with the hypothetical distribution generated by applying these rules. Instead, the result would be more or less similar to the hypothetical distribution. The result of an actual series of tosses is presented below.

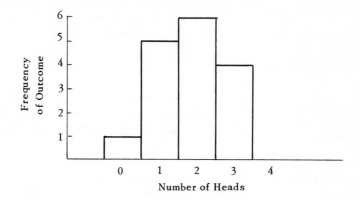

Fig. 18. Results of tossing four coins 16 times.

This distribution is somewhat different from the hypothetical distribution, yet it is quite similar in its general shape. In this case it can be said that the *model* provided by the hypothetical distribution is a rather good approximation of the results of an actual empirical (experimental) test.

Hypothetical distributions are used as models from which to make predictions about the occurrence of actual observed events. If the measurements are found to be quite similar to the hypothetical distribution, confidence in the *appropriateness* of the model is increased. It should be emphasized that the mathematical rules are never disproved; if the observed results and the hypothetical distribution are highly dissimilar, the conclusion is that the actual conditions do not meet the assumptions. For example, a biased die will produce results that do not agree with a hypothetical distribution based upon the assumption of an unbiased die.

Empirical distributions seldom_____
exactly with the hypothetical probability
distribution.

1    agree                    _____

When an empirical frequency distribution is
quite similar to the hypothetical frequency
distribution, confidence in the hypothetical
distribution as a_____ is increased.

2    model                    _____

If tossing a coin resulted in many more
heads than tails, we would suspect that
the coin is_____.

4    biased                   _____

Lack of agreement between empirical tests
and mathematical models never disproves
the_____.

3    models                   _____

1

It is often possible to make a hypothesis, based on probability, about an experimental outcome or series of outcomes. If the outcome approximates the results predicted by the hypothesis, the hypothesis is considered appropriate. If, on the other hand, the results have little correspondence with the hypothetically predicted results, the hypothesis is rejected.

2

3

Consider the following simple, but typical, experimental procedure. A naive white rat is placed in a maze with a single choice point at which it may turn either to the right or left. The initial hypothesis might be that the rat is equally likely to turn in either direction. According to this hypothesis the probability of a right turn on any trial is 1/2. Each trial is independent, so the probability of two successive right turns is, according to the multiplicative rule, equal to the product of the probabilities of each turn: $1/2 \cdot 1/2 = 1/4$. The probability of a left turn on any trial is also 1/2, and the probability of a left and then a right turn is 1/4.

4

How many consecutive turns in either direction would lead to the rejection of the hypothesis that right and left turns are equally likely? Suppose the rat makes seven consecutive right turns. The probability of this outcome, according to the initial hypothesis, is $1/2 \cdot 1/2 \cdot 1/2 \cdot 1/2 \cdot 1/2 \cdot 1/2 \cdot 1/2 = 1/128$. The probability of seven consecutive left turns is also 1/128. The probability of either seven consecutive right turns or seven consecutive left turns is 2/128. In other words, the odds against either of these outcomes is 128 to 2. Such odds would strongly suggest that the initial hypothesis was incorrect and should be rejected. It should be noted that any combination of seven consecutive turns has a probability of 1/128, but a combination that includes both left and right turns is not a consecutive series of turns in a single direction.

When the results of an experiment do not correspond to the results predicted by a hypothesis, the hypothesis is_____.

1    rejected

Suppose an event has only two possible outcomes. The hypothesis that each is equally likely can be stated in terms of probability. The probability of one of the outcomes occurring is_____.

2    $\frac{1}{2}$

Suppose the rat in the example made one left turn and six right turns. This outcome could occur in the following combinations:

LRRRRRR,    RLRRRRR,
RRLRRRR,    RRRLRRR,
RRRRLRR,    RRRRRLR,
RRRRRRL.

The probability of one left and six right turns is_____ in 128.

4    7

Suppose the rat in the example has made three consecutive right turns. According to the initial hypothesis, the probability that the rat will turn right on the fourth trial is _____.

3    $\frac{1}{2}$

1     When the number of coins in a sample is increased, the number of possible outcomes is increased. The hypothetical distribution becomes more complex but its general shape remains the same. Figure 19 represents the hypothetical distribution for eight coins and 256 tosses.

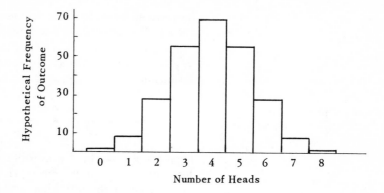

Fig. 19. Expected frequency of outcomes when eight coins are tossed 256 times.

2     If the number of alternatives were increased until each bar on the histogram blended with the next, the result would be like a distribution which is already familiar: it would be like the normal

3     probability distribution that was described in Chapter 5. Many of the variables that concern the psychologist are best represented by such a distribution. It is known, for example, that intelligence

4     differs among individuals. Intelligence test scores demonstrate that most people are relatively typical but that some extreme cases do occur. Members of the population who are mentally deficient occur infrequently enough to be considered oddities, and extreme intellectual superiority is also considered unusual because it appears so infrequently. Studies of intelligence, based upon extensive samples of the population, have shown that the distribution of intelligence test scores approximates a normal distribution.

Although the number of possible outcomes is increased as the coin sample size is increased, the general shape of the hypothetical _____ remains the same.

1 distribution (model)
_____

The smooth curve which is shaped much like the hypothetical distribution curve in Figure 19 is the_____distribution curve.

2 normal
_____

Many variables of interest in psychology are best_____by a normal distribution model.

3 represented (described)
_____

If intelligence is normally distributed, most people are nearly_____in intelligence.

4 average (typical)
_____

If a characteristic is normally distributed, extreme cases occur_____.

5 infrequently
_____

# Chapter 8

# EXPERIMENTAL APPLICATIONS

Most research concerned with behavioral phenomena is directed toward the discovery of basic principles that can be applied with some generality. These principles are usually based upon observations of a limited number of cases selected from the total group that is the concern of the experimenter. The total group is called the *population,* the experimental subgroup is the *sample.* The statistical method of generalizing from the sample to the population is called *statistical inference.* Statistical inference is the most important statistical application used in research.

The measures which describe the characteristics of a population are known as *parameters.* Determining the parameters of the population is usually too expensive or time-consuming to be accomplished. Therefore, statistics obtained from measures of a sample are used to estimate the values of parameters of the population. Conclusions based upon sample observations are made with a certain degree of risk. The risk may be stated in terms of the probability of error and can thus be represented quantitatively.

To minimize the risk of error in generalizing about a population from knowledge of a sample, certain precautions must be taken. It would be inappropriate, for example, to draw conclusions about the average intelligence of high school graduates if the sample of this population included only college freshmen. A large subclass of the basic population would not be represented in such a sample.

Statistical inference is a technique which permits an experimenter to _____ from a sample.

1    generalize

_____

A generalized principle applies to a large group of cases. Such a group is called a _____.

2    population

_____

When it is impossible to measure every case in a population, the mean of a sample may be used as an _____ of the population mean.

3    estimate

_____

A sample should not be used if it excludes a subclass of the _____.

5    population

_____

Generalizations regarding population parameters are always made with some degree of _____.

4    risk

_____

1    Samples that do not accurately represent the population from which
they are drawn are called *biased* samples. The sample must be
2    representative if generalizations are to be justified. Representative
sampling can be assured only if every case in the population has
an equal chance of being selected.

The most typical technique is to derive the sample by *random
selection*. This means that all cases in the population constitute
3    a common pool of cases from which the sample is drawn. A refinement of the randomized sampling technique is *stratified sampling*.
In this method, the population is grouped into subclasses and the
subclasses are sampled according to their proportional representa-
4    tion in the population. In stratified sampling every case still has
an equal probability of being selected, but due to the categorizing
process the size of subclasses in the sample is proportional to
their size in the population. This helps to assure that uncontrolled
selection factors will not cause disproportional representation of
some classes in the sample.

Randomized selection is a goal seldom attained in most studies.
Rather the samples are selected from available segments of the
5    total population. There is little danger in this procedure if the
available segments are representative of the total population. But
this is seldom known. Conclusions about a population, based upon
sampling procedures that violate the basic requirement of randomized selection, should be considered tentative at best. Further
tests should precede general acceptance of such conclusions.

A sample that excludes certain kinds of cases in a population is a_____sample.

1    biased

_____

Random selection insures that each case in the population has an equal opportunity of being_____.

2    chosen (selected)

_____

The population is divided into subclasses, and the subclasses are sampled according to their proportional representation in the population. This sampling technique is known as_____sampling.

3    stratified

_____

Stratified sampling assures that the subclasses in the population are represented in the sample in the same_____as in the population.

4    proportions

_____

Samples that are selected because they are available are seldom known to be completely _____of the population.

5    representative

_____

1
2
The population mean can never be predicted exactly from a sample that does not include every case in the population. Since the characteristics of the sample only approximate those of the population, the sample is used to determine a range of values which have a high probability of including the population mean. The size of this range of values depends on two factors, the size of the sample and the variability of the population.

3
As the size of the sample increases, the probability that the sample is like the population increases. The efficiency of increasing the size of the sample as a method of increasing the precision of the estimate of the population mean is related to the square root of the sample size. This means that a sample must be made four times as large in order to reduce the probable error of estimating the population by one half. In other words, there is a practical limitation on the estimating efficiency gained by increasing the sample size. Small samples may be increased by four times their original size without increasing cost and labor excessively, but if the sample is originally extensive, increasing the size may not be worth the expense.

4
5
The variability in the population is unknown and must be estimated from the sample variability. The estimate is somewhat biased but a correction is made in the estimate to offset this. It is important when considering conclusions based upon sample distributions to recognize that they are dependent upon the factors of sample size and sample variability. The precision of an estimate increases as the size of the sample increases and as the variability of the sample decreases. The remainder of the chapter describes how these principles are used in designing an experiment.

Since a population mean cannot be determined exactly from a sample, it is usually estimated to lie within a_____of values.

1    range

_____

The size of the range of values that most probably contains the population mean depends upon the_____and_____of the sample.

2    size *(N)*

      variability

_____

The range of a population mean is estimated from a sample of $N = 25$. To decrease this range by one half would require a sample of $N =$_____.

3    100

_____

As the variability of a sample decreases, the precision of an estimate of the population mean_____.

5    increases

_____

Both sample size and sample variability influence the precision of an estimate of the_____ _____.

4    population mean

_____

Suppose an educator wants to study the influence of distracting stimuli on learning efficiency. He decides to compare the learning rate in a quiet room in the library with the learning rate in the college cafeteria during the lunch hour. Two students are selected from a college population and given the same study materials, which they study for the same amount of time. One student studies in the library, the other studies in the cafeteria. A test measuring learning is given to the students at the end of the learning period, and the test scores are compared.

Suppose the test results indicate that the student who studied in the cafeteria learned more than the student who studied in the library. Does this result demonstrate the superiority of study under distracting conditions?

1     Such a conclusion is unwarranted. Many extraneous influences could have caused the result. The subjects might differ greatly in their ability to learn, in their motivation to learn, or in their previ-
2     ous experience with the material studied. Any of these influences might have confounded the result — that is, the difference in learning might have been caused by some factor other than amount of distraction.

3     These possible extraneous influences must be controlled before a conclusion about the effects of distraction is justified. This would be true, of course, even if the student in the library had shown superiority in learning. No matter what the results obtained, an experimenter would be unwilling to draw any conclusions when the data are based on so few subjects and could be influenced by so many uncontrolled factors.

Conclusions based on a difference in the performance of two subjects are generally unjustified, because the difference may be the result of_____factors.

1     extraneous (many)          _____

An experimental result is said to be confounded when a factor other than the one being considered influences the_____ of the experiment.

2     outcome (result)          _____

When an extraneous factor exists and may affect the outcome of an experiment, this factor has not been adequately_____.

3     controlled          _____

In reality, an educator interested in the effects of distractive stimuli on learning would introduce safeguards to minimize the possibility of error. There are two ways to refine the experiment and improve

1  the dependability of the outcome. One method is to carefully control such factors as ability and motivation in order to minimize their influence. It should be noted, however, that it is impractical, if not impossible, to control all the factors that might influence the ex-

2  perimental outcome. The other refinement is to use many students as subjects in both conditions — not to eliminate the influence of the extraneous factors, but to balance the effects of these factors by providing a large number of cases in each condition. The assumption is that differences will be equally represented in each

3  sample. As the size of the samples increases, the probability of attaining the required balance increases. In most experimental designs, a combination of the two approaches is adopted to reduce the probability that extraneous influences will affect the outcome.

When an experimenter increases the sample size to balance the effects of extraneous factors, he is making use of the principles of probability to reduce the likelihood of error. When he selects a random sample of the population he is interested in, he expects the variations in the sample — variations that might confound the re-

4  sults — to be normally distributed. In other words, when a population is sampled the factors, such as intelligence and motivation, that may differ from individual to individual will be represented in the sample in a normal distribution — just as height or weight are in studies concerned with physical dimensions.

When an experimenter wishes to limit the effect of a particular factor that could confound his results, he uses a method by which the factor can be_____.

1    controlled
_____

Increasing the size of a sample of subjects helps assure that the influence of extraneous factors is_____.

2    balanced
_____

The probability of successfully balancing the extraneous influences in an experiment is directly related to the_____of the sample.

3    size
_____

If a factor such as height, for example, is normally distributed in a population, it should also be normally distributed in a _____of that population.

4    sample
_____

A graphical analysis will illustrate the reasoning behind the methods of experimental design. In a sample of college students drawn at random from a college population, variations in learning ability should follow a normal distribution. Graphically, then, the general learning ability in the sample could be represented by a normal curve. Figure 20 shows such a distribution.

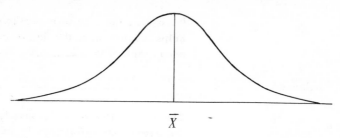

Fig. 20. Hypothetical curve of learning ability in a random sample of college students.

Suppose this sample of subjects is randomly assigned into sub-groups. Each subgroup then serves as the sample for an experimental condition. In the experiment concerned with distracting stimuli, two subgroups are required — one for the quiet environment, the other for the distracting environment. Before exposure to the experimental conditions, the average or mean learning ability should be approximately the same for both subgroups. The groups should also be similar in their variability; thus the variance and the standard deviation of each subgroup should be about the same. If the environmental factors introduced in the experiment cause a difference in the learning rates of the subgroups, then the means of the two subgroups, as measured by the tests covering the material learned, should be quite different after exposure to the experimental conditions.

It is usually assumed that the best graphic representation of a random sample of a normal population is a_____distribution curve.

1      normal

_____

If the subjects in a sample are randomly assigned into subgroups, the means of the subgroups are expected to be approximately _____.

2      equal (the same)

_____

Both the mean and the_____of randomly assigned subgroups of a random sample should be highly similar.

3      standard deviation (variability)

_____

The effect of subjecting subgroups of a random sample to different environmental conditions would be evidenced by a difference between the_____of the subgroups.

4      means

_____

The steps described on page 114 are shown graphically in Figure
21. Dividing the sample (represented by the broken line) into two
subgroups by random methods should yield subgroups that are quite
similar, both in their average learning ability and in their variation.
Any differences should be the result of chance variations in the
randomized division of the sample. The distributions of the subgroups should be approximately like those represented by the two
solid-line curves.

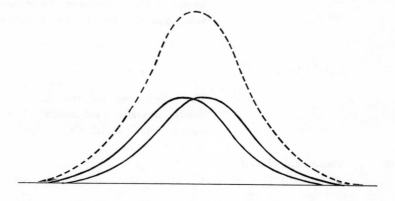

Fig. 21. Hypothetical curves of two groups drawn from a random
sample of college students.

It makes no difference which subgroup is made the experimental
group and which is made the control group. Whatever differences
exist would not be great enough to make the subgroups statistically
different.

The distributions of two subgroups of a
random sample should be about_____.

1      the same             _____

When subgroups are formed by randomly
dividing a sample, differences between
the subgroups are the result of_____
factors in the selection process.

2      chance             _____

Two subgroups of a random sample are
assigned to different experimental conditions. Presumably the subgroups, before
undergoing the experimental treatment, are
_____ .

3      equal             _____

1    The next step in the experimental procedure is to assign the sub-groups to the experimental conditions. In the example, Group I might be assigned to the quiet library, Group II to the cafeteria and its lunch-hour distractions.

2    After the subjects in the subgroups have undergone the experimental conditions, the test results should indicate whether the different conditions had a sufficiently different influence upon the groups to cause a difference in their performance.

3    If the two groups, which were representative of a common population before the experiment, are now distinguishable on the learning test, the curves of the scores on the test should be easily distinguishable. And if the distractions interrupted the learning process, the test scores of Group II should be lower than those of Group I — as shown in Figure 22.

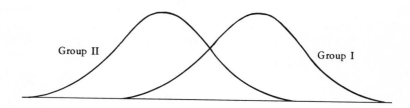

Fig. 22.  Hypothetical curves of scores of Group I and Group II on the learning test.

4    If the curves now are clearly different, it is reasonable to assume that the experimental conditions have changed the subgroups so that they are no longer two samples of a single population but instead represent two populations which differ on the dimension being measured.

If the subgroups of a sample have only slight differences, attributable to chance, they may be assigned to the experimental conditions as if they were_____.

1    equal (the same)                    _____

If the experimental conditions influence the subgroups differently, these subgroups can no longer be considered_____.

2    equal (the same)                    _____

At the beginning of the experiment the subgroups were selected to represent a common or single_____.

3    population                          _____

If, as a result of the experiment, the difference between the subgroups is statistically significant, we say each subgroup now represents a_____population.

4    different                           _____

1    Statistical tests are available to determine whether differences between the means of subgroups are great enough to be attributed primarily to the effect of the experimental conditions and not to chance factors arising in the assignment of the subjects into the subgroups. These tests depend on two descriptive measures of the subgroups, the means and the standard deviations. The statistical question is: Is the difference between the means of the subgroups too great to be attributed to chance variations in the sampling process? The variation within the subgroups is used to estimate how much of the variation is attributable to chance factors.

2    The statistical test used is called the test for the significance of difference between the means. If the results are significant, the experimenter can conclude with a prescribed probability that the two subgroups, chosen from a sample of a common population, now represent two different populations on the dimension being measured. It is concluded that this change from two samples or subgroups of a single population to two groups representing different populations on the dimension being measured is a result of the ex-

3    perimental manipulations. If this is the case, the change shows the hypothesis concerning the conditions to be statistically tenable within the limits of the possible error reported, and the difference is said to be statistically significant.

4    The characteristics of the normal probability distribution that has been used as the model preclude our eliminating every possible error in drawing conclusions. The interpretation of the experimental results should include a statement of the level of significance attained. The same statistical reasoning may also be applied to other statistics, such as those representing variation and correlation, and the resulting reports are presented in comparable fashion.

To determine whether group differences are best explained by chance factors or by experimental factors, one makes use of statistical tests that depend on the standard deviations and the _____ of the subgroups.

1    means                    _____

If differences between groups are sufficiently great, the differences cannot be attributed to _____ factors.

2    chance                   _____

If chance factors cannot reasonably account for group differences, the groups are said to differ to a degree that is statistically _____ .

3    significant              _____

Obtaining absolutely certain results is impossible because of the characteristics of the normal probability curve, which is used as a statistical _____ .

4    model                    _____

1
2     Statistical verification of experimental results is stated in the
      language of probability. Since verification may have important
      implications, the odds supporting any conclusions must be fairly
      strong. A gambler might be happy to gamble if the odds favoring his
      winning were two to one. In psychological research such odds are
      not strong enough to lead to the acceptance of a hypothesis.

3     The *levels of confidence* usually considered sufficient to reject
      the explanation of chance are the 5 per cent or the .05 level and
      the 1 per cent or the .01 level. If the probability of the results
      occurring by chance is .05, the probability of the results having
      occurred because of the experimental manipulations is .95. In
      common odds, this would mean the odds against the results occur-
      ring by chance are 19 to 1. If the .01 level is met, the odds are
      99 to 1. The actual statistics which are used will not be included
      here because this would require a more detailed discussion of the
      principles of probability. Even without a detailed analysis, how-
      ever, the meaning of significance levels can be appreciated by the
4     casual reader of experimental results. When such significance levels
      are combined with the careful control of any variables that might
      bias experimental results, the conclusions drawn are sufficiently
5     trustworthy to be accepted as scientific data. When, despite such
      precautions, some doubt remains, a repetition of the experiment is
      possible.

The experimenter who performs an experiment to verify a hypothesis would require that the results be verified by_____ methods.

1    statistical                          _____

The likelihood that an outcome is due to manipulation of the experimental variables and is not the result of chance is stated in terms of_____.

2    odds (probability)                   _____

The probabilities or odds usually thought sufficient to reject the possibility that a result is due to chance are_____or

_____.

3    19 to 1 (.05)                        _____

     99 to 1 (.01)                        _____

The use of statistics does not preclude the need for careful_____of variables in the design of psychological experiments.

4    control                              _____

When experimental results are not conclusive, the study should be_____for further verification.

5    repeated                             _____

1
2    In experiments in which it is possible to control for the influence
     of factors that do not specifically pertain to the variables being
     considered but which may influence the experimental outcomes,
     such controls may lead to an increase in the precision of the ex-
3    periment. This precision results from a reduction in the variability
     of the sample. Graphically this is represented in Figure 23.

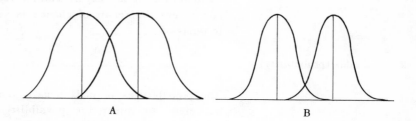

Fig. 23.  Hypothetical curves of experimental subgroups.

4    Both pairs of subgroups have been subjected to the same experi-
     mental conditions, and the difference between the means is the
     same in both pairs. But the variability within the subgroups of the
     pair A is greater than the variability in the subgroups of the pair B.
     Statistically, the pair of samples with the least area of overlap of
     the two curves (pair B) will show the greatest probability of group
     differences. Thus by reducing the variability in the subgroups, it
     may be possible to emphasize the influence of the experimental
     conditions.

Introducing experimental refinements by controlling factors that might influence the results adds_____to the design of an experiment.

1      precision

                                    _____

In deciding which factors to control, the experimenter chooses those variables that he feels will have the greatest_____ on the results.

2      influence

                                    _____

Controls are effective if they reduce the _____of the subgroups in the experimental conditions.

3      variability

                                    _____

As the sample variability decreases, the difference between sample means that is required for statistical significance will (increase/decrease).

4      decrease

                                    _____

# Chapter 9

# RELIABILITY AND VALIDITY OF PSYCHOLOGICAL MEASURES

1   All measurements are estimates. The diameter of a steel bar can be measured very precisely with a micrometer caliper, but if several measurements of the bar are made they will differ slightly from each other. The average of these measurements is the best estimate of the diameter. This average is not the *exact* diameter; several

2   measurements are combined to make a good *estimate*. The estimate can be improved by making more measurements but the diameter can never be determined exactly.

Measurements are affected by the conditions under which they are made. The diameter of the steel bar will be greater on a warm day than on a cold day because metals expand as the temperature increases. Temperature causes a change in the diameter of the bar and in the length of the calipers.

The same problems of measurement exist in psychological experi-

3   mentation. Behavior can not be measured precisely because it changes from time to time, because the devices used to measure it are not perfectly accurate, and because the measuring devices may change with time.

4   Measurement is also complicated by the fact that the measuring device itself may affect what is being measured. We can measure the temperature of water in a glass by means of a thermometer. But if the thermometer is colder than the water, it will lower the temperature of the water slightly when it is put in the glass. In similar fashion in psychology, behavior may change simply as a result of its being measured. Suppose a person's ability to solve arithmetic problems is measured by timing him while he works

5   problems. The first trial permits him to practice and on his next trial he will very likely do better. Thus his skill is increased because the device used to measure the skill permits him to practice while he is being measured.

Measurements are not exact but rather are
_____ of the quantities measured.

1    estimates                    _____

In general, an estimate becomes more
accurate the more_____one can com-
bine to arrive at the estimate.

2    measurements                 _____

Exact measurement of behavior is not possible. One reason for this is the fact that
an organism's behavior_____from time
to time.

3    changes (varies)             _____

Psychological measurements are often in-
accurate because the behavior being measured is often _____ by the measuring device itself.

4    changed (affected)           _____

Sometimes a psychological measuring device permits a subject to_____while
he is being measured, thus making later
scores different.

5    practice                     _____

Despite the difficulties described, measurement is not a hopeless
1    task. Although it is impossible to measure behavior with absolute
2    accuracy, useful estimates can be made. Further, statistical tools
can be used to determine how precisely a measurement has been
estimated.

A familiar statistic used to estimate behavior is the arithmetic
3    mean. The arithmetic mean of a series of measurements of an individual's reaction time, for instance, is an estimate of the true
4    reaction time of the individual. The obtained mean probably is not
exactly his normal reaction time, but it is a good estimate of this
reaction time.

The question of precision of the estimate of a measurement can be
stated as follows: How good is the measuring device itself, and how
5    stable is the trait being measured? This question may be partially
answered in terms of the *reliability*, or consistency, with which the
6    device measures behavior from one time to another. The statistic
that describes the reliability of a measuring device is the *coefficient of reliability*. Actually, the coefficient of reliability is a
correlation coefficient. It is calculated by the method described in
Chapter 6, and a similar algebraic notation is used. The symbol
often used to represent the coefficient of reliability is $r_{xx}$. The
formula for obtaining $r_{xx}$ is:

$$r_{xx} = \frac{\Sigma x_1 x_2}{N s_{x1} s_{x2}},$$

where    $x_1 = (X_1 - \overline{X}_1)$ for the initial measurements
$x_2 = (X_2 - \overline{X}_2)$ for the second set of measurements
$s_{x1}$ = the standard deviation of the set of initial
measurements
$s_{x2}$ = the standard deviation of the second set of
measurements.

It is not possible to measure an organism's behavior with absolute_____.

1    accuracy                   _____

It is possible to determine how precisely a measurement has been estimated by making use of_____tools.

2    statistical                _____

The arithmetic mean of a series of measurements of behavior is an_____of the true behavior.

3    estimate                   _____

A single measurement can be used as an estimate of an individual's behavior, but a more accurate estimate can be obtained by finding the_____of a series of measurements of the behavior.

4    mean                       _____

Technically speaking, a psychological measuring device that yields consistent measurements is said to be_____.

5    reliable                   _____

The statistic that describes the consistency with which a measuring device measures is the coefficient of_____.

6    reliability                _____

An example will help to show what the coefficient of reliability means and how it is calculated. Suppose each subject in a group assembles a number of identical small bolts, washers, and nuts. Each subject is allowed two minutes for the task; his score is the number of assemblies completed. Three weeks later the same individuals attempt the same task. The measurements to be compared are the scores made on the two occasions. The question of consistency or reliability is: Is the performance of the subjects on the second occasion consistent with their performance on the first occasion? In technical terms, is this measure of manual dexterity reliable? It is assumed that the relative ability of the subjects is unchanged and that any discrepancies from their initial ranking are due to the unreliability of the measuring device.

Assume that fifty individuals are tested on two occasions with the result that

$$\overline{X}_1 = \overline{X}_2 = 20$$
$s_{x1} = 3.6$ assemblies in two minutes on the first occasion
$s_{x2} = 3.8$ assemblies in two minutes on the second occasion
$\Sigma x_1 x_2 = 633.$

Then

$$r_{xx} = \frac{\Sigma x_1 x_2}{N s_{x1} s_{x2}}$$

$$= \frac{633}{50(3.6)(3.8)}$$

$$= \frac{633}{684}$$

$$= .93$$

The reliability of a psychological measuring device can be determined by using the device on the same group of subjects at different_____ .

1    times

---

The consistency of a measuring device in yielding similar results at different times is known as_____ .

2    reliability

---

The coefficient of reliability is obtained by testing a group on two occasions. The coefficient will not be accurate if the relative ability of the subjects_____during the interval between measurements.

3    changes

---

If the relative standing of subjects on a second administration of a test is different from their standing on the test when it was first given, and if their relative ability has not changed in the interval between measurements, then the measure is not_____ .

4    reliable

---

Subjects are asked to interpret from photographs a series of facial expressions intended to show various emotions. The series is judged by the same subjects a few weeks later. Score is the number of expressions correctly interpreted.

$N = 35, \quad s_{x1} = 5.2, \quad s_{x2} = 5.4, \quad \Sigma x_1 x_2 = 294.$

5    .30        $r_{xx} = $ _____ .

1
2    As is the case with any correlation coefficient, the coefficient
of reliability can not exceed 1.00. A coefficient of 1.00 indicates
perfect reliability. The correlation of .93 obtained in the example
indicates a fairly high degree of reliability. Hence, results obtained
3    in using this measuring device are quite reproducible. A particular
subject's performance on one occasion predicts his performance on
a second occasion within fairly close limits. People who are at one
end of the range when measured the first time are at the same end
of the range when measured again. Subjects near the mean on a first
occasion are also near the mean on a second occasion.

4    In the example given on page 130, the mean of the first set of
measures was the same as the mean of the second set. In actual
practice this seldom occurs. Usually there is at least a small
practice effect. That is, all the subjects become a little more
proficient through practicing whatever is being measured. This
causes a shift in the mean on the second and subsequent trials.

If the practice effect were the same for all subjects, or if benefits
from practice were directly related to position in the range, this
shift would cause no difficulty with the reliability coefficient.
Unfortunately, the amount that subjects benefit from practice is
often not in proportion to their position in the distribution. Thus
a certain amount of error creeps into reliability coefficients when
5    practice can affect later performance. If time is allowed to elapse
between the first and the second trials, in hopes that forgetting will
reduce the practice effect, other errors may arise from differences
in forgetting, in opportunity to practice during the interval, and so
6    on. Despite these difficulties, the resulting errors are usually small
and if the coefficient is high (near 1.00) the errors are considered
insignificant.

The maximum possible value of the coefficient of reliability is _____ .

1     1.00

If a coefficient of reliability is about 0.0, the reliability is very (large/small).

2     small

If a measure is very reliable, a person's performance will be about the _____ on one occasion as on another.

3     same

If the mean of the scores of a group of subjects measured on a given occasion is the same as the mean of their scores on a later occasion, it is pretty safe to say there was no _____ effect.

4     practice

The major reason for delaying the second set of measurements when determining a measure's reliability is to _____ the effects of _____ .

5     reduce

      practice

Practice effect must be zero if a measure is to be useful in predicting later performance.

6     false          true _____ false _____

The procedure just discussed is called the *test-retest* method. Subjects are tested, later they are retested, and the correlation between the test and the retest scores is determined. Reliability coefficients obtained by the test-retest method are subject to certain errors. Some of these errors, such as the practice effect, can be avoided by using the *split-half* method. The split-half method is a means of estimating the *internal* consistency of a psychological measuring device by comparing scores made on one half of it with scores made on the other half.

Basic to the use of the split-half method is the assumption that if a measuring device is reliable, all components of the device must measure the same attribute or group of attributes. The method is ordinarily applied to psychological tests made up of a large number of items, all of which are intended to measure a single ability or closely related group of abilities. If all of the items measure virtually the same factor, performance on one half of them ought to be the same as on the other half, within the limits of measurement error.

There are many ways in which a measure can be split into two halves. Score on the first half of the test could be compared with score on the last half. Combined score on the first and fourth quarters could be compared with combined score on the second and third quarters, and so on. However, a few closely related items might be clustered together, or fatigue might cause the person to perform erratically or guess more toward the end of the test. Therefore, the split is usually made by grouping the odd-numbered items together to obtain one score and the even-numbered items together to get the other score. If the test is internally consistent, every subject should get about the same score on the odd-numbered items as he gets on the even-numbered items.

The split-half method of obtaining the coefficient of_____eliminates the effect
of_____.

1    reliability

    practice

The split-half method determines reliability
by measuring the internal_____of the
test.

2    consistency

The split-half method of determining reliability should be used only if all items of
the measuring device are supposed to measure approximately the_____factor.

3    same

To obtain the split-half reliability coefficient, subjects' scores on odd-numbered
items *must* be compared with their scores
on even-numbered items.

4    false

    true_____ false_____

If a test is_____consistent, the scores
subjects make on odd-numbered items ought
to be about the same as the scores they
make on even-numbered items.

5    internally

1    Suppose that a split-half reliability coefficient of .88 is obtained on a test. This indicates a high degree of similarity between the two artificial half-tests. It can be shown mathematically, however, that if the two half tests were each as long as the one that was split, the reliability coefficient would have been even larger. The artificial cutting of the test into two parts reduced the obtained reliability coefficient slightly.

It is possible by means of a formula to estimate the correlation that could have been obtained from a full length test identical to the two half-tests used. This formula, known as the Spearman-Brown formula, is

$$r_2 = \frac{2r_1}{1 + r_1},$$

2    where $r_2$ is the estimated value of the reliability coefficient for the full-length test, and $r_1$ is the value of $r$ obtained by the split-half method from the two half-tests.

3
$$r_2 = \frac{2(.88)}{1 + .88} = \frac{1.76}{1.88} = .94.$$

4
5    The value given by the Spearman-Brown formula is an improved estimate of the reliability coefficient, but it may not be precisely correct because it is based on certain assumptions about the similarity of the two half-tests. Nevertheless, it provides a method of estimating reliability that is useful when the test-retest method is not feasible.

The reliability coefficient obtained by the split-half method is_____than it would have been if two similar full-length tests had been compared.

1    lower (less)    _____

In the Spearman-Brown formula, $r_2$ stands for the estimated_____ of_____ the measure would have if the full-length measure had been used instead of the split-halves.

2    coefficient    _____

reliability    _____

An achievement test is given to students in a college class in psychology. The split-half reliability is .80. The reliability coefficient, corrected by the Spearman-Brown formula, is_____.

3    .89    _____

The value of $r$ found by the Spearman-Brown formula is not a "true" measure of reliability. It is an_____of the value $r$ would have if the full length of the test could be used to obtain $r$.

4    estimate    _____

The true value of $r$ for the psychology test is probably about_____.

5    .89    _____

1    Besides being reliable, a psychological measure must also be *valid*. A valid measure is one that measures what it is supposed to measure.

2    In the physical world it is obvious to us that distance can be measured by means of a yardstick, a tape measure, or a ruler. These are all valid measures of distance. In the realm of psychology, however, it is not often so clear that a measure is valid, because it is necessary to use overt behavior to infer mental processes or to predict later behavior. In psychology we can measure the *effects* of mental processes but not the *processes* themselves.

3    The manual dexterity test already discussed illustrates two aspects of validity. Assembling bolts, washers and nuts can be accepted operationally as a measure of manual dexterity. That is, manual dexterity is defined in such terms as to include this sort of manipulation of objects. *Operational* validity exists when the task performed fits a well-defined psychological concept.

4    
5    The assembly task may also have *predictive* validity. A psychological measure has predictive validity if its results can be used to predict other behavior. The skill and speed with which a subject assembles small parts often gives an indication of his success in certain kinds of work. Hence, a test that measures manual dexterity may be used to select job applicants because it predicts their success or failure on the job.

6    Similarly, an electronics trouble-shooting aptitude test may have both operational and predictive validity. It may, and probably does, indicate how much a person knows about electronics. It may also predict how successful he will be at learning or performing a specific job.

A psychological device that measures what it is intended to measure is _____.

1     valid

           _____

Only the _____ of mental processes can be measured directly; the processes themselves can not.

2     effects

           _____

If a test measures a trait that is defined b₃ the nature of the task, the test has what is technically known as _____ validity.

3     operational

           _____

A measure that can be used to forecast the future behavior of a subject has _____ validity.

4     predictive

           _____

A psychological measure may have both predictive and operational _____.

6     validity

           _____

If it turned out that color-blind people are better automobile drivers, a test of color blindness would have high _____ validity for selecting good drivers.

5     predictive

           _____

1   Predictive validity is determined by comparing the scores subjects
2   make on the predictor (usually a psychological test) with the scores
3   they make on the *criterion*. The criterion is some measure of the
later behavior that one wants to predict. For example, the small-
part assembly task might be used as a selection test by a company
engaged in light manufacturing. The assembly task would be the
predictor, and the criterion would be success on the job.

4   Validity is measured in terms of a *coefficient of validity*. The
validity coefficient is a correlation coefficient, usually the Pearson
product-moment coefficient of correlation, in which the independent
*(X)* variable is the predictor and the dependent *(Y)* variable is the
criterion. Thus the formula is the familiar

$$r_{xy} = \frac{\Sigma xy}{N s_x s_y} \ .$$

Suppose an electronics trouble-shooting aptitude test is given to 25
trainees. After two months in a company training program, their success in the training program is evaluated by an instructor who
scores their ability to solve trouble-shooting problems. The question
is: Did the aptitude test predict the outcome of training?   On the
aptitude test the standard deviation *(s_x)* was 10.0. The standard
deviation of scores on the problem-solving test *(s_y)* was 8.5. The
sum of the cross products of the deviation scores ($\Sigma xy$) was 1275.
From this information,

5

$$r_{xy} = \frac{1275}{25(10.0)(8.5)} = \frac{1275}{2125} = .60.$$

When a test is used to predict later behavior, the behavior so predicted is called the _____.

1    criterion

---

An aptitude test used for the selection of applicants to a university is an example of a _____ .

2    predictor

---

If an aptitude test is used to predict success in a class in school, the criterion for determining the_____of the test is likely to be the grades the students receive at the end of the course.

3    validity

---

In obtaining the coefficient of validity for an aptitude measure, scores on the aptitude test are taken as the_____variable.

4    independent $(X)$

---

Thirty subjects were tested to see whether intelligence test scores $(Y)$ could be predicted from heart rate $(X)$. It turned out that $s_x = 5.4$, $s_y = 11.0$, and the sum of cross products was $\Sigma xy = 500$. It can be said that in this experiment intelligence test scores and heart rate are (a) not related, (b) slightly related, (c) highly related.

5    b $(r_{xy} = .28)$

---

1    A validity coefficient of .60 is fairly typical of aptitude tests used to predict learning. As with any Pearson $r$, perfect predictive validity $(r = 1.00)$ is impossible to achieve in the practical situation. Too many factors conspire to reduce the validity coefficient:

2    a. The predictor test is not perfectly reliable. Hence the obtained scores are not the true ones, and it is necessary to begin with an imperfect measuring device.

3    b. The criterion score is also unreliable, perhaps even more unreliable than the predictor. In the example, the criterion score reflected a demonstration of skill which may have been evaluated rather subjectively by the instructor. On a different occasion, the instructor's ratings might have been quite different.

4    c. Scores on any psychological measure are affected by the motivation of the subject. In terms of the example, suppose a subject had been highly motivated to get the job, and worked especially hard on the aptitude test. If he later found himself uninterested in the work, he would do poorly on the performance measure. His change in motivation, reflected in his test scores, would make the test appear less valid, though really the "error" then is in the individual and not in the test.

5    These are only some of the factors that cause predictions to be less accurate than hoped for. All of these factors introduce errors into scores, thus reducing validity and lowering the validity coefficients.

A validity coefficient of 1.00 is (a) never, (b) seldom, (c) frequently, (d) usually, found in practical prediction problems.

1    (a)                            _____

One reason predictor measures are never perfectly valid is that they are never perfectly_____.

2    reliable                       _____

Both_____ and predictor are often unreliable.

3    criterion                      _____

A person becomes very interested in a subject after he has taken an aptitude test. Because he studies hard, his criterion score is likely to be (higher/lower) than the score the aptitude test predicted for him.

4    higher                         _____

Errors in the predictor scores, errors in the criterion scores, and changes in motivation all have the effect of (increasing/decreasing) validity coefficients.

5    decreasing                     _____

# Chapter 10

# INDIVIDUAL DIFFERENCES AND NORMS

1  It is often desirable to compare individuals on the basis of some specific aspect of their behavior. Consider, for example, Jack, a twenty-year-old student in a music school, and Jim, a forty-year-old mechanic. Both are administered a test of auditory perception. Jack's score is 162 and Jim's is 135. Thus we know they differ in at least three measurable attributes: age, auditory acuity, and occupation. Of course, they differ in many other measurable attributes as well.

2  Before making comparisons such as those noted for Jack and Jim, the purpose of the comparison must be well understood and the selection of individuals to be compared must be undertaken in a logically defensible manner. Our purpose in administering the auditory perception test might have been to find out what constitutes typical performance among men in general on the perceptual task presented. This would justify administering such a test to individuals who are so different in other respects.

We probably would not include Jim in a sample which was to be used to select applicants to a music school. In that situation we would want to compare the test performance of students already in the school with their success in the school, in order to determine how test scores relate to success in school and, hence, how high a score is needed before an individual can reasonably be expected to succeed in the school.

3
4  Technically speaking, then, the population to which individuals belong must be well defined before there is an adequate basis for making comparisons of individual performances. In the example,
5  both Jack and Jim belong to the population of "men-in-general," but only Jack belongs to the population of music students.

A score of 162 on the auditory perception
test is above the mean.

true_____   false _____

not indicated_____

1    not indicated

Before comparisons are made, the_____
to be used in the comparison must be selected in a logical manner.

2    individuals    _____

Mary is a student in a secretarial school.
Jane is a liberal arts student in college.
Both are given a test of clerical speed and
accuracy. Both Mary and Jane belong to a
_____that might be designated as
"women-in-general."

3    population    _____

Of the two girls who took the clerical
speed and accuracy test, only_____
belongs to the population of liberal arts
students.

4    Jane    _____

The student whose score should be used
in determining the clerical speed and accuracy of college students is_____.

5    Jane    _____

1    Once a population is properly defined, it is possible to test or measure the behavior of individuals comprising a sample on the assumption that the performance of individuals in the sample is typical of the behavior of all individuals in the population. Measures obtained from such samples are said to be *standardized*.

2
3
4    Data obtained in the standardization process are called *norms*. In the original usage of the term, a norm was only an estimated mean of a population. More recently, norms have come to include measures of variability, so that an individual's score can be compared with the expected scores of *all* individuals in the population. To continue with our example, assume the mean score of music majors to be 140. Then, so far as Jack is concerned, his score of 162 tells us only that he is above the norm, or mean, of 140. If we know also that the standard deviation of scores is 10, we can see at once that his score is nearly at the top of the distribution.

5    When tables of norms are intended for use in school situations, they often show means for students according to age or grade placement in school. Such tables sometimes lead to the mistaken conclusion that a high score indicates that the subject is capable of performance at a much higher age or grade level. Actually such tables show only what is normal, or average, performance at each age or grade. A high score, therefore, only indicates that the subject is performing above average in comparison with his peers. Norms that permit comparison of an individual with all members of his class yield much more information, are less likely to be misinterpreted, and hence are usually much to be preferred. Nevertheless, both types of norms are discussed in this chapter because both are widely used and should be understood.

Measures of behavior that are obtained from representative samples of well-defined populations are _____ measures.

1    standardized

Data obtained in the process of standardization are called _____.

2    norms

The mean of a representative sample may be used as the _____ for the population from which the sample was taken.

3    norm

Norms on most modern tests include measures of _____ . Thus a given subject's score can be compared with the expected scores of _____ the individuals in a population.

4    variability

     all

Misinterpretation of norms is *more* likely if the norms are based on (a) means only, (b) means and variabilities of population samples.

5    (a) means only

Many measurable abilities change with age, particularly during the period from birth to adulthood. However, a method of measurement may be suitable over a range of several years. When this is the case, norms may be established at yearly or half-yearly intervals. With this kind of measure, a particular raw score will be the mean for one age and a different raw score will be the mean for another age. Norms of this sort are called *age norms*. They are frequently used with measures of intelligence. An example of a set of age norms is given in Table 11.

### Table 11
### Relation of Raw Score to Age on XYZ Intelligence Test

| Raw score | Mental age |
|-----------|------------|
| 140 | 15 |
| 135 | 14 |
| 125 | 13 |
| 110 | 12 |
| 95 | 11 |
| 80 | 10 |
| 65 | 9 |

This table indicates that a person who has a raw score of 110 is performing at a level typical of twelve-year-olds. If he scores 132 he is performing almost as well as a typical fourteen-year-old. If his score is 95 he is doing only as well as the average eleven-year-old. Thus a person's mental age can be estimated from his raw score on the test.

Once a person's mental age has been determined, his *intelligence quotient* is easily obtained by means of the formula

$$\text{I.Q.} = 100 \times \frac{\text{mental age}}{\text{chronological age}}.$$

Thus if a twelve-year-old child has a raw score of 125 on the test, his mental age is thirteen and his I.Q. is:

$$\text{I.Q.} = 100 \times \frac{13}{12} = 108.$$

Norms which describe test scores in terms of the means obtained by children of various ages are called _____ norms.

1  age

_____

Suppose a ten-year-old got a raw score of 135 on the XYZ intelligence test. His score is the same as that obtained by the average child of age _____.

2  fourteen

_____

A fifteen-year-old of below-average intelligence would get a raw score on the XYZ test below _____.

3  140

_____

A twelve-year-old who gets a score of 95 on the XYZ intelligence test has an estimated mental age of _____.

4  eleven

_____

A twelve-year-old who gets a raw score of 95 on the XYZ test has an I.Q. of _____.

5  92

_____

1      Norms for tests used in school situations are often based on the
       various grade levels for which the test is appropriate. Table 12
       illustrates a set of *grade norms*.

## Table 12
2
3      ## Grade Norms for the ABC Achievement Test

| School grade: | | Mean raw score |
| Year | Month | |
|------|-------|----------------|
| 12 | 0 | 210 |
| 11 | 8 | 208 |
| 11 | 6 | 200 |
| 11 | 4 | 189 |
| 11 | 2 | 175 |
| 11 | 0 | 167 |
| 10 | 8 | 165 |
| 10 | 6 | 155 |
| 10 | 4 | 142 |
| 10 | 2 | 127 |
| 10 | 0 | 110 |

By means of this table of norms, the score of any individual taking
the test can be related to the performance of individuals at the
various grade levels. Thus whatever his actual grade placement is,
a student who has a raw score of 189 on the ABC test is at the
level of the average person in the fourth month of his eleventh
school year.

4      A refinement of the grade norm is the *age-within-grade* norm. When
       age-within-grade norms are established, the standardizing sample
       is made up only of students who are at the proper grade placement
       for their age. Thus students who are in a particular grade because
       of acceleration or retardation are not included in developing the
5      norms. This keeps the norms from being affected by dull older
       students or bright younger students.

If a sample based on grade in school includes children without regard to age, the norms obtained would be_____norms.

1     grade

-------------------------------------------

When grade norms are based on samples that include only those who are in the normal age range for their grade, the norms obtained are_____ _____ _____ norms.

4     age-within-grade

-------------------------------------------

Age-within-grade norms are probably better than grade norms because they exclude any _____ young children and_____ older children who are not at proper grade placement for their ages.

5     bright

       dull

-------------------------------------------

An average beginning eleventh-grader who takes the ABC test would be expected to get a raw score of_____.

2     167

-------------------------------------------

A tenth-grader whose grade placement is 10 years 4 months gets a score of 142 on the ABC test. If he takes the test again on entering the eleventh grade, the score he will most likely receive is_____.

3     167

-------------------------------------------

The norms thus far discussed only permit comparisons between an individual's score and the mean of a population. It is often important to know more precisely where the individual stands with respect to others in his own population. To go back to the music student, Jack — just how good is his auditory perception score of 162 when compared with other music majors? Suppose that the mean for this group is 175 and the standard deviation is 30. From this information a table can be constructed showing how many standard deviations a particular score is from the mean.

### Table 13
### Standard Scores for Music Majors
### on the Auditory Perception Test

| Raw score | $z$ score |
|-----------|-----------|
| 265 | 3.0 |
| 250 | 2.5 |
| 235 | 2.0 |
| 220 | 1.5 |
| 205 | 1.0 |
| 190 | 0.5 |
| 175 | 0.0 |
| 160 | −0.5 |
| 145 | −1.0 |
| 130 | −1.5 |
| 115 | −2.0 |
| 100 | −2.5 |
| 85 | −3.0 |

The table shows that Jack's score of 162 is about 0.4 standard deviations below the mean. In the same way, the score of any student can be compared with the normative group by means of Table 13, and a $z$ score can be obtained.

Norms discussed thus far only permit comparison of an individual's performance with the _____ performance of a group.

1    mean
_____

The mean performance does not give enough information to permit adequate comparison of a person's score with each of the others in his own _____.

2    population
_____

An individual's $z$ score is the number of _____ _____ his score is from the mean of the sample he is compared with.

3    standard deviations
_____

Jim got a raw score of 135 on the auditory perception test. This gives him a $z$ score of about _____.

4    −1.3
_____

Actually it is inappropriate to compare Jim's score with the norms in Table 13, because Jim is not a _____ _____.

5    music major
_____

Suppose applicants to a music department are tested and found to have a score distribution like that in Table 13. What should the admission cut-off score be if only 50 per cent of the applicants can be admitted?

6    175
_____

1

2

The $z$ score is not very convenient to use because scores below the mean are always negative. There are two ways in which $z$ score norms can be converted to a more easily used form. One way is to convert to percentile scores, which show the percentage of subjects in the standardization sample scoring below each raw score. The other way is to make use of transformed scores, which are determined by applying the following transformation formula:

3

4

transformed score = an arbitrary mean +
$z$ × an arbitrary standard deviation.

A common transformation is that in which the arbitrary mean is 50 and the standard deviation is 10. Scores so transformed are called $T$ scores. Table 14 shows the auditory-perception-score norms converted to $T$ scores.

Table 14

5

6

$T$ scores for Music Majors on the Auditory Perception Test

| Raw score | $z$ score | $T$ score |
|---|---|---|
| 265 | 3.0 | 80 |
| 250 | 2.5 | 75 |
| 235 | 2.0 | 70 |
| 220 | 1.5 | 65 |
| 205 | 1.0 | 60 |
| 190 | 0.5 | 55 |
| 175 | 0.0 | 50 |
| 160 | −0.5 | 45 |
| 145 | −1.0 | 40 |
| 130 | −1.5 | 35 |
| 115 | −2.0 | 30 |
| 100 | −2.5 | 25 |
| 85 | −3.0 | 20 |

Thus Jack's raw score of 162 is equivalent to a $T$ score of approximately 46.

In a $z$ score distribution, scores below the mean are always _____ .

1  negative

_____

Centile scores show what _____ of the sample subjects fell below the corresponding raw score.

2  percentage

_____

When a $z$ score is put into the expression $50 + 10z$, the resulting number is called a _____ score.

3  $T$ (transformed)

_____

According to Table 14, a person having a raw score of 220 on the auditory perception test would have a $T$ score of approximately _____ .

5  65

_____

An individual who gets a $T$ score of 36 on the auditory perception test has scored _____ standard deviations _____ the mean.

6  1.4

below

_____

A test has a mean of 75 and a standard deviation of 12. A subject obtains a raw score of 93. His $T$ score is _____ .

4  65

1     Group norms are frequently presented as centile ranks. An individual's centile rank indicates what percentage of the normative
sample received scores lower than he did. Most statistics texts
provide tables that permit simple transformations from $z$ scores to
centile ranks. Table 15 shows $z$ scores and related centile ranks
for the auditory perception test.

## Table 15
## Centile Ranks for Music Majors on the Auditory Perception Test

2
3
4

| Raw score | $z$ score | Centile rank |
|-----------|-----------|--------------|
| 245 | 2.33 | 99 |
| 237 | 2.05 | 98 |
| 225 | 1.65 | 95 |
| 213 | 1.28 | 90 |
| 200 | .84 | 80 |
| 191 | .52 | 70 |
| 183 | .25 | 60 |
| 175 | .00 | 50 |
| 167 | −.25 | 40 |
| 159 | −.52 | 30 |
| 150 | −.84 | 20 |
| 137 | −1.28 | 10 |
| 125 | −1.65 | 5 |
| 113 | −2.05 | 2 |
| 105 | −2.33 | 1 |

Jack's raw score of 162 places him between the thirtieth and
fortieth centiles at about the thirty-fifth centile.

A centile rank indicates what percentage of subjects in a normative sample received raw scores_____than a particular value.

1  lower

_____

For music majors, a centile rank of 65 on the auditory perception test is equivalent to a raw score of about_____.

2  187

_____

According to Table 15, a raw score of 121 is equivalent to a centile rank of about _____.

3  4

_____

A centile rank of 98 on the auditory perception test represents a raw score of 237. This means that_____ per cent of the subjects in the normative sample received raw scores lower than_____.

4  98

   237

_____

It is easy to look up a person's centile rank, $z$ score, grade standing, or $T$ score in a table of norms, but in using them one is likely
to overlook possible pitfalls.

1    a. Norms are no better than the sample used to obtain them. The
group tested must be a good sample of the population it is
supposed to represent. It is not likely that all music students
could be used to develop the norms for the auditory perception
test. The sample used must be representative of the whole
population.

2    b. Unless the local group on which the test is being used is like
the population on which the norms are based, it may be inappropriate to set up cut-off scores based on the population
norms. If the music school has very high standards, its own
norms may be higher than the published norms.

3    c. Some norms tend to get out of date. If the test is old, a new
set of norms may be needed because the population has
changed. The quality of music students may change over a
period of years.

4    d. Raw scores are not "true" scores. We saw in Chapter 9 that
measurement is never perfect. The raw score obtained by an
individual is an estimate of his true score, and tables of norms
should indicate how good this estimate is.

Unless all of these factors are taken into account, more meaning
may be inferred from a table than the data warrant.

In establishing norms, the group tested must be_____ of the population which the norms are supposed to reflect.

1        representative

---

Norms may get out of date because of changes that take place in the_____ they represent.

3        population

---

An individual's_____ score is not necessarily his true score.

4        raw

---

One must be sure the group he is testing is like the_____ upon which the norms are based before he makes comparisons or draws conclusions about the adequacy of his group's performance.

2        population

---

# CRITERION TEST

This test consists of fifty multiple-choice questions based on the material in Chapters 2 through 10. It may be used to check your understanding of the material and to indicate what portions of it should be reviewed. The answer to each question appears immediately below the question. Cover the answer until you have circled the response that seems most appropriate. When you miss a question, review the material indicated by the page reference that follows the answer.

1. Statistical methods that describe data in easily understood, summarizing statements are called: (a) descriptive statistics, (b) codified data, (c) inferential statistics, (d) raw data.

a, p. 22

2. A table made by tallying experimental results to show the number of subjects obtaining each possible raw score is: (a) a frequency polygon, (b) a frequency distribution, (c) a normal polygon, (d) a normal distribution.

b, p. 24

3. A graph that indicates the frequency of events by means of a series of adjacent rectangles is called: (a) a histogram, (b) a pie diagram, (c) a frequency polygon, (d) a rectangular polygon.

a, p. 28

4. If we wish to plot two or more distributions on the same graph, it is usually best to use: (a) frequency polygons, (b) histograms, (c) frequency distributions, (d) chance curves.

a, p. 32

5. If you add together all the scores of a group of subjects, and divide by the number of subjects, you obtain the: (a) mode, (b) median, (c) mean, (d) medial value.

c, p. 36

Use the following information to answer questions 6 through 9. Two groups of rats were used to test the effectiveness of two conditioned stimuli. Trials to criterion for the members of the two groups were

Group A: 10, 12, 14, 15, 16, 17, 17, 17, 18, 18,
18, 18, 19, 19, 19, 20, 21, 22, 24, 26.
Group B: 10, 14, 15, 17, 17, 17, 17, 17, 17, 18,
18, 18, 18, 19, 19, 20, 20, 21, 22, 25.

6. The median score for Group A is: (a) 16, (b) 17, (c) 18, (d) 19.

c, p. 42

7. Compared to Group A, Group B has: (a) smaller skew and greater range, (b) greater variance and smaller range, (c) smaller skew and smaller range, (d) greater skew and smaller range.

d, pp. 42, 46

8. Of the following, the *only* statement that is true is: (a) The mean of Group B is 17. (b) The mean of Group A is 17. (c) The mode of Group B is 17. (d) The mode of Group A is 17.

c, p. 44

9. Of the following, the *only* statement that is true is: (a) The range of Group A is smaller than the range of Group B. (b) The variance of Group B is smaller than the variance of Group A. (c) The standard deviation of Group A is smaller than the standard deviation of Group B. (d) both groups have the same variance.

b, pp. 46, 52

10. The expression "$\Sigma X$" indicates that one should: (a) add up all the measurements, (b) find the mean of the distribution, (c) separate the data into two or more groups, (d) make a graph showing all of the data.

a, p. 38

11. In statistics it is conventional to use the symbol $\overline{X}$ to represent: (a) any raw score, (b) a particular raw score, (c) the mean of a distribution, (d) the sum of all the raw scores.

c, p. 38

12. The principle defect of the range is that it: (a) does not tell how far the highest score is from the lowest, (b) does not distinguish between mean deviation and standard deviation, (c) is not based on all the scores in the distribution, (d) is not as readily computed as other measures of variability.

c, p. 46

13. A deviation score is: (a) the difference between a raw score and the mean, (b) the standard deviation, (c) the same as a raw score, (d) the difference between a raw score and the variance.

a, p. 48

14. The scores that have the greatest effect on the value of the variance are those: (a) above the mean, (b) below the mean, (c) nearest the mean, (d) farthest from the mean.

d, p. 52

15. Another way of expressing $\dfrac{\Sigma(X - \overline{X})^2}{N}$ is:

(a) $\sqrt{\dfrac{\Sigma(X - \overline{X})}{N}}$,  (b) $\dfrac{\Sigma x^2}{N}$,  (c) $\dfrac{(X - X)^2}{\Sigma N}$,  (d) $\left(\sqrt{\dfrac{\Sigma(X - \overline{X})}{N}}\right)^2$.

b, p. 52

16. The standard deviation is: (a) the square of the mean deviation, (b) the square root of the mean deviation, (c) the square of the variance, (d) the square root of the variance.

d, p. 58

17. In a normal distribution, approximately 95% of the cases lie between: (a) ±3s, (b) ±6s, (c) −1s and +1s, (d) −2s and +2s.

d, p. 62

18. In a normal distribution the percentage of scores lying above the mean: (a) is about 95%, (b) is about 68%, (c) is 50%, (d) depends upon the skew of the distribution.

c, p. 64

19. A standard score: (a) is a measure of central tendency, (b) is a deviation score divided by the standard deviation, (c) is found by subtracting the mean from the raw score, (d) is a centile score.

b, p. 66

20. In a normal distribution: (a) all standard scores are positive in sign, (b) all standard scores are negative in sign, (c) half of the standard scores are negative in sign, (d) the number of scores of positive sign depends upon the skew of the distribution.

c, p. 68

21. The mean of a raw score distribution is 54, and the standard deviation is 10. A student with a standard score of 0 has a raw score of: (a) 0, (b) 44, (c) 54, (d) 64.

c, p. 70

22. An essential condition for a bivariate analysis, as distinguished from other statistical treatments, is that observations be: (a) made on human beings, (b) unrelated, (c) made at the same time or at least on the same day, (d) paired.

d, p. 72

23. The statistic that indicates the degree of relationship between two variables is the: (a) semi-interquartile range, (b) coefficient of relationship, (c) correlation coefficient, (d) variance.

c, p. 74

24. If two measures have a high positive correlation, and a person has a low score on one measure, his score on the other measure should be: (a) high, (b) low, (c) the same score, (d) a score the value of which depends on whether one variable is the cause of the other variable.

b, p. 76

25. If $\Sigma xy = 160, s_x = 4, s_y = 5$, and $N = 10$, then $r$ is: (a) .50, (b) .80, (c) .83, (d) 8.0.

b, p. 82

26. Height and weight are positively but not highly correlated. Mary is below average in height. Therefore Mary: (a) certainly weighs less than average, (b) is likely to weigh less than average, (c) is likely to weigh more than average, (d) certainly weighs more than average.

b, p. 86

27. If the probability of the occurrence of an event is 1, this means the event: (a) can't occur, (b) is unlikely to occur, (c) is likely to occur, (d) is certain to occur.

d, p. 88

28. If we toss an unbiased die, the probability of obtaining a 2 on the first toss is (a) 1/6, (b) 1/2, (c) 2, (d) 6.

a, p. 90

29. The probability that a couple's first two children will be girls: (a) is about 1/2, (b) is about 1/4, (c) is about 2, (d) depends on how many children they ultimately have.

b, p. 92

30. If ten coins are tossed, the most likely result is: (a) 5 heads and 5 tails, (b) 4 heads and 6 tails, (c) 6 heads and 4 tails, (d) all the above are equally likely.

a, p. 96

31. A mathematically calculated distribution curve that closely describes a distribution found in nature is said to be: (a) a model, (b) a statistic, (c) an empirical curve, (d) biased.

a, p. 98

32. The parameters of a population are often difficult to measure because the population is large. Therefore, estimates of these parameters are sought from: (a) nature, (b) samples of the population, (c) authorities on the subject, (d) smaller populations.

b, p. 104

33. The most accurate statement about the problem of controlling extraneous factors in an experiment is: (a) It is impossible to control all the factors that might affect the experiment. (b) Extraneous factors can be expected to cancel each other. (c) Extraneous factors must be eliminated. (d) All known extraneous factors must be eliminated.

a, p. 112

34. The difference between two groups is said to be significant if the difference in their means: (a) could not have occurred by chance, (b) is not likely to be the result of chance, (c) could have occurred by chance about half of the time, (d) might have occurred by chance less than half the time.

b, p. 120

35. If the factor of intelligence is normally distributed in a population, the distribution of this factor in a random sample of the population should be: (a) skewed, (b) normal, (c) bimodal, (d) any of the above.

b, p. 116

36. The results of an experiment are said to be confounded when: (a) they contradict previous research findings, (b) they are surprising, (c) they are influenced by extraneous factors, (d) they confirm previous research findings.

c, p. 110

37. If two samples are selected at random from a single population, it is most likely that: (a) their means and standard deviations are about the same, (b) their means and standard deviations are quite different, (c) their means are similar but their standard deviations are quite different, (d) their means are quite different but their standard deviations are about the same.

a, p. 114

38. After an experiment is completed, the distribution curves of the experimental and control groups are significantly different. It is most appropriate to conclude that the groups: (a) should be recombined, (b) represent different populations, (c) are valueless for further experimentation, (d) have been affected by extraneous factors.

b, p. 118

39. Several measurements of a kind of behavior are usually obtained when one wants to determine: (a) the best estimate of the true value, (b) the true value of the variable, (c) how the true value of the variable varies, (d) how many observations are needed to determine the exact value of the variable.

a, p. 126

40. The consistency of a psychological measuring device is reflected in a statistic called the coefficient of: (a) consistency, (b) reliability, (c) calibration, (d) validity.

b, p. 128

41. Of the following, the most reliable psychological measuring device would be one having an $r_{xx}$ of: (a) $-.80$, (b) $-.10$, (c) $+.20$, (d) $+.90$.

d, p. 132

42. When the correlation of subjects' scores on even-numbered test items with their scores on odd-numbered items is high, the test: (a) is valid, (b) has a high coefficient of variability, (c) has high split-half reliability, (d) has balanced reliability.

c, p. 134

43. A test item appears unsuitable for inclusion in an aptitude test but is effective in discriminating between good and poor job applicants. The item: (a) has predictive validity, (b) should be rejected because it appears useless, (c) should be rewritten to make it look better, (d) is likely to be unreliable.

a, p. 138

44. Four tests are tried out as predictors of success in a college. The tests correlate with later success in college as follows: test A, $r = .27$; test B, $r = -.09$; test C, $r = -.41$; test D, $r = .65$. The best test for selecting students is test: (a) A, (b) B, (c) C, (d) D.

d, p. 142

45. Technically speaking, the norm of a population is: (a) the behavior that is normal in the population, (b) the mean performance of individuals in a random sample of the population, (c) the range of performance measures obtained from the population, (d) the variability of behavior within a sample of the population.

b, p. 146

46. If a child of 12 has an I.Q. of 120, his mental age is: (a) 10.0, (b) 12.0, (c) 14.4, (d) 18.8.

c, p. 148

47. Most sixteen-year-olds are in the eleventh grade. Norms based on a sample of all children in the eleventh grade would be: (a) age norms, (b) grade norms, (c) age-within-grade norms, (d) none of the above.

b, p. 150

48. A measure of behavior is said to be standardized if it is based on: (a) the entire population concerned, (b) a representative sample of the population concerned, (c) extensive statistical treatment of data obtained, (d) at least 100 individuals from the population concerned.

b, p. 146

49. In a z score distribution, scores below the mean are always: (a) positive, (b) less than 1, (c) greater than 1, (d) negative.

d, p. 154

50. Norms may get out of date because: (a) statistical methods change from time to time, (b) the sample used to obtain the norms was not representative of the population, (c) the sample gets too old for the population, (d) changes take place in the population the norms represent.

d, p. 158